QL   Porter
644   The world of the frog
.P65   and the toad

Date Due

			JUL 1992
			APR '87
			OCT '82

Kalamazoo Valley Community College
Kalamazoo, Michigan 49001

PRINTED IN U.S.A.

THE WORLD OF THE FROG AND THE TOAD

A LIVING WORLD BOOK
John K. Terres, Editor

LIVING WORLD BOOKS
John K. Terres, Editor

The World of the **Frog** and the **Toad**

Text and Photographs by
George Porter

J. B. LIPPINCOTT COMPANY
Philadelphia & New York

To Doris

All photographs in this book were taken by the author, unless otherwise specified.

Contents

Author's Introduction

MY INTEREST IN FROGS goes back to my early childhood. I clearly remember one evening when I was six or seven years old and my mother was playing chamber music with Fritz Kreisler. In the music room I had a terrarium containing several tree frogs, and, as soon as the music started, the frogs chimed in—to the amazement and, I remember, annoyance of the great violinist, and of my mother and father. But not of my grandmother, who had helped me catch the frogs. I do not remember whether this deterred Mr. Kreisler from returning, but it surely did not stop me from bringing frogs into the house. Nearly half a century has passed since then, but my interest in frogs remains unabated.

When John K. Terres suggested that I write a book about frogs and toads I gladly agreed, in the hope that I might thus instill in others some of the fascination which these creatures have held for me practically all my life. This book is not intended to be a textbook on herpetology or a handbook on frogs and toads. Rather, I would like to share some of my personal observations and experiences. As there are about 100 species of frogs and their allies in the United States alone, it would, of course, have been impossible for me to deal with all of them within the framework of this book. I have, therefore, concentrated on a select few representative, or otherwise noteworthy, species.

I am deeply grateful for the help given to me by many of my friends, and for their assistance in obtaining live specimens to study and photograph. Thus, in alphabetical order, I want to thank James Anderson, John Borneman, Roland Clement, Ronalda Keith, Frank Ligas, Les Line, Duryea Morton, Dick Pasqual, Stanley Quickmire, Alexander Sprunt, 4th, and, deeply, J. Albert Starkey. I also want to thank my editor, John K. Terres, and certainly not least, my wife Doris for her superhuman patience.

GEORGE PORTER

New York
March 1967

Meet the
Frogs and the Toads

ONE OF THE QUESTIONS I am frequently asked is: "What is the difference between a frog and a toad?" It may surprise you to know that this is not an easy question to answer. In the United States and Canada alone there are seven groups—or, more correctly, families—comprising the animals commonly called frogs and toads. Each of these families consists of several genera, and each genus usually consists of many species, for an impressive total of nearly one hundred. Among the seven families there is one which is called true frogs (Ranidae) and another one called true toads (Bufonidae). Perhaps because "frog" and "toad" are the only one-word names in the English language for any member of the order of tailless amphibians, and perhaps because true frogs and true toads are the most commonly seen members of this order, it is a general impression that all the various jumping, leaping, hopping, swimming, croaking animals are either frogs or toads. One need not be a naturalist to tell a true frog from a true toad. Frogs have a smooth, moist skin, are usually slender, have long hind legs which make them excellent jumpers, and are commonly found in or near water. Toads, on the other hand, have a dry, rough skin with warts (some of which, however, are glands), are stocky, with relatively short legs, hop rather than jump, and are usually found away from water, in the woods, in gardens, and sometimes in cellars.

13

The Gulf Coast toad is a true toad.

Although the English names for the tailless amphibians (most frogs and toads) are so limited and undescriptive, the scientific nomenclature is much richer. Most frequently used is the Latin name *salientia* meaning "the jumping ones," but there are also alternate names in both Latin and Greek, *acaudata* and *anura,* both meaning "tailless." This helps to differentiate them from the other order of amphibians, the salamanders, which are called *caudata* or *urodela,* both words meaning "tailed." The word "amphibian" is itself derived from the Greek *amphi* and *bios,* meaning "double life," from their usual beginnings in water, and their later lives on land.

Almost all members of this class of vertebrates, tailed and tailless alike, have a strong tie to the water, even though the majority of them live primarily on land, or part of the time in water, in a semiaquatic life. They are classified somewhere between the lower class of fishes and the higher class of reptiles, and were probably the first vertebrates which, in the Devonian period of the Paleozoic era, some 400 million years ago, emerged from the water to take up life on land. Most of them, however, have not divested themselves entirely of their dependence upon water. It is there that their life cycle begins after the adults lay their gelatinous eggs in the ponds. The gilled larvae of salamanders, frogs, and toads, emerging from the eggs, are not equipped for life on land and have to take their oxygen from the water in the same way that fishes do. Gradually they transform into terrestrial air-breathing creatures. This transformation, called metamorphosis, may take a few weeks or several years depending on the species, and some salamanders never transform into land-living creatures at all.

However, all tailless amphibians (frogs and toads) do transform and eventually take up life on land, though many choose to remain close to the water always. The larvae of salamanders more or less resemble

The bullfrog is a true frog.

the adults, for they retain a tail even after the completion of their metamorphosis, but the larvae of frogs and toads, called tadpoles or pollywogs, differ so greatly from the adults that one who did not know their future could not guess that these wiggly creatures, all head and tail, are destined eventually to become frogs or toads.

In addition to being descendants of the first amphibian that crawled out of the water, the frogs and toads have another "first" to their credit. In that silent world, many millions of years ago, the first sound ever produced by means of vocal cords was made by a creature resembling a frog or a toad. The only other sounds produced by living things at that time were the chirping, rasping and buzzing of insects which, then as now, are not emitted by vocal cords.

The sounds produced by today's frogs and toads are of great variety, each species having its own particular call. The high-pitched whistle of the spring peeper and the low sonorous grunt of the bullfrog are familiar to anyone with even fleeting outdoor experience, but there are many other calls—croaking, whistling, snoring, clicking, chirping, trilling, and grunting—which are as helpful in identifying the various species as bird calls are in bird identification. But, while most birds are active during the day, frogs and toads are primarily creatures of the night, and their multivoiced calls add magic to the beauty of the darkness. Frogs and toads have always fascinated artists and naturalists and children, and their almost grotesque appearance attracts even the most casual eye. We find them jumping across the road on a rainy spring evening, we disturb them in cellars or under porches, we hear them plunge into the water as we stroll around the edge of a pond. What, then, are these creatures? How do they live? What is their life cycle? To seek the answers to these questions, not only from books and laboratories but also from personal observation, is a rewarding experience. I shall attempt to share this experience with you by showing the wondrous world of the frogs and toads.

Spring

MY HOME is in New York City, a place hardly conducive to nature exploring. Yet, a drive of only an hour or so will take me into nearby Westchester County where, with some searching, one can still find open land. Raccoons, skunks, foxes and opossums are plentiful there and deer are abundant. A buck once leaped across the hood of my automobile on the main street of Bedford Village, New York, without attracting too much attention, and, in the autumn, deer can frequently be seen in the yards of homes in the more rural neighborhoods. The drumming of grouse can be heard in the woods, and on many a lake the great blue heron is not an uncommon sight.

By the middle of March much of the snow is gone. The woods and meadows are still bleak, but a closer look at the tips of the twigs reveals the beginning of buds. The ground is wet from the melted snow and early spring rains, and little shoe-shaped puddles appear wherever we step. Here and there, among last autumn's decaying leaves and in occasional snow patches, the tips of skunk cabbage emerge from the soggy ground. Hardly any of the spring birds have as yet arrived. The woods are almost completely silent, with only the occasional whistle of the black-capped chickadee and the caw of the crow interrupting the stillness. Throughout the woods little streamlets and dribbles of water have filled the depressions in the ground. These waters will have disap-

Spotted salamander.

Spermatophores of the spotted salamander.

peared by summer, but while they last they are life-giving breeding pools, for it is in these temporary ponds that much amphibian life starts. Some of these ponds are still bordered with thin patches and scallops of ice and, with the exception of some aquatic insects which scurry busily about, they seem still and dead. Life within them, however, has already begun.

Although a woods pond at first glance looks black and opaque, a moment spent peering into it suddenly reveals that it is much sunnier than at first imagined, and full of subdued color. The bottom is layered blackish brown from years of fallen leaves, topped with the soft orange of last autumn's maple and oak trees, contrasting with swirls of yellow-green slime. And, curiously, the pool bottom seems to be polka-dotted. Many of the submerged leaves are spotted with small white specks, with some areas being literally covered with them. Curiosity makes us fish out one of the leaves, and we find that the white specks are small gelatinous pyramids, glistening and quivering on the leaf to which they are attached. They are spermatophores, or sperm capsules, probably deposited only the night before by the male spotted salamander, *Ambystoma maculatum*. The female spotted salamanders will swim or crawl over these spermatophores and take them into their bodies through the cloaca, and then they will lay their eggs. The courtship of the spotted salamander is spectacular but rarely observed, as it takes place at night

18

Spermatophores of the spotted salamander greatly enlarged.

when large numbers of these salamanders congregrate in the breeding pools which churn and boil with the twisting, milling swarm of yellow-spotted black bodies. After a few nights all will be over: the salamanders will return to the land as silently as they came and all that will remain in the pond will be the gelatinous egg masses attached to submerged twigs and leaves. The large greenish egg masses of the wood frog, which lays its eggs later, will frequently be found close to those of the spotted salamander, but they are distinguishable by their looser consistency and by containing a much larger number of eggs.

The ponds warm only slowly in the weak sunlight and chill March air. The frogs which have been sleeping in the mud beneath the water all winter have not as yet felt the signal that will tell them that spring is

The egg masses of the spotted salamanders resemble balls of cotton or tapioca pudding.

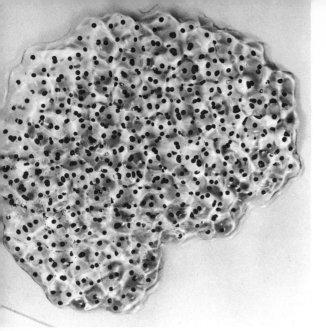

The egg mass of the wood frog contains a much larger number of eggs than does the egg mass of the spotted salamander.

near. Something is stirring, however, for the woods are full of a rough, low-pitched "kraa-arrak-kraakk"—a sound like the creaking of a wheel in need of oil, although some believe it resembles the quacking of ducks. To many it is a sound heard with pleasure, for this is the courtship call of the wood frog, *Rana sylvatica,* one of the first frogs to mate in the spring. Eager to see these harbingers we push through a thicket of brier and bramble to find the pond suddenly still and apparently devoid of frogs. The first rule for anyone to follow for successful wildlife watching is to remain completely still and motionless. If you must move, do so slowly and quietly. If possible remain hidden behind a tree or other object, and the creature you want to observe will accept you as part of the landscape and resume its activities.

After a few minutes, a spreadeagled frog appears on the surface of the water, as though propelled from the bottom of the pond. And then another and another. Their drab skins blend with the dead leaves, and it is hard to believe that these are the same frogs that once they leave the breeding pool, will be conspicuous in their beautiful bronze color and raccoonlike black facial mask.

Soon one of the frogs farthest from us ventures a call, and gradually more and more join the growing chorus. As with most frogs and toads, only the males call. In doing so the wood frogs distend their throats and the sides of their bodies so that they present an oddly swollen appearance. Several mating pairs are now swimming about, the male astride and tightly clasping the female, in a position to fertilize her eggs as she lays them. These egg masses, or clusters, which may contain as many as 2,500 eggs, are enclosed in a gelatinous substance which gradually swells after being deposited in the water. Sometimes the mass may become larger than the frog that laid it. Unfortunately the wood frogs frequently lay their egg masses, attached to twigs, grasses and other submerged objects, close to the edges of the ponds. Even slight evaporation and subsidence of the water may leave the egg masses partially exposed to the air and thus extremely vulnerable to changes in the weather. This early in March freezing is frequent at night, and any of the eggs that have been held in the ice will almost certainly die, although the remaining, submerged eggs in the mass may continue to develop to hatching. Evaporation of water and freezing of the eggs are not the only hazards which threaten the embryos within the egg mass. Saprolegnia, a fungus disease, often infects and swiftly kills large quantities of eggs.

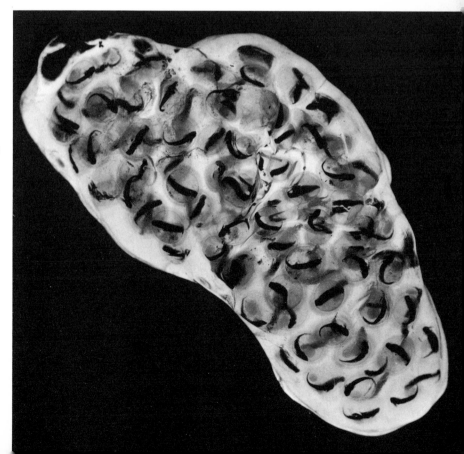

Egg mass of spotted salamander with embryos beginning to develop.

The World of the Frog and the Toad

Gradually, gray clouds have obscured the sun, and a chill wind and a few snow flurries remind us that it is still pre-spring and that winter is not, as yet, completely gone. The sudden drop in temperature has silenced the frogs. Their mating is almost finished, and within a few days they will leave the breeding pools to return to the woods.

March is nearly over. The days grow longer and the feel of spring is in the air. Although the trees have not yet developed the silvery green halo of leaves about to appear, the tips of the twigs are beginning to turn green and to look alive and healthy, instead of the sleeping brown they have been all winter. Every rock in the woods glistens with its running rivulets which form small pools in an earth too wet to absorb any more water. The ground is still brown, with no apparent new growth, but in

Spring peeper calling.

The spring peeper carries on its back a large mark resembling an X.

the shelter of an oak's roots we find the first hepatica, the delicate pastel flowers, light blue or pink, or lavender, or white, framed by last year's fleshy leaves.

Suddenly the quiet of the woods is broken by the put-put-put-put-r-r-r-rt of a motorboat in the distance. It is a moment before our mind correctly records the sound, and we realize that it is really the drumming of a ruffed grouse on the hillside above us. Most of our meetings with grouse happen unexpectedly and startlingly, for the large bird will suddenly take off almost from under our feet with an explosive whirl of his wings. I once was fortunate enough to discover a male drumming, and managed to watch him without his being aware of me. He stood on a log, a large reddish-brown bird, that looked like an expensive, exotic chicken with a large neck ruff. He beat his wings slowly at first to create the drumming sound, then increased the beat rapidly until it ended in a hollow roll. During the time I watched, the grouse repeated his drumming every few minutes, regularly, with no variation. It is a moment like this that makes wildlife observation, even with any attendant discomfort, worth while. The long hours spent at the expense of cold, wet feet are forgotten, and our interest is rekindled, along with a renewed consciousness of the season's changes.

I believe that each of us keeps his own calendar of the seasons and that, probably subconsciously, it is usually some particular object enjoyed in childhood rambles that tells us when spring has arrived. Many are alerted by the flaming green of skunk cabbage, others have a special feeling for the yellow-green haze around a bare weeping willow tree, or the soft silver catkins on a pussy willow. Some await the first long call of a red-winged blackbird, the golden masses of forsythia, or the sight of a robin strutting on a lawn. There are even a few, with a very late clock indeed, who must see the woods blue with violets before they will acknowledge spring's arrival. To me, however, all these symbols must yield before the silver piping, the call like distant sleigh bells, of the spring peeper, *Hyla crucifer,* the true herald of spring.

24

Eggs of spring peeper.

*Tadpoles of spring peeper
—greatly enlarged.*

For the past two weeks we have heard an occasional individual peeper call, as though testing its voice before the entire chorus began. Today, however, it is warm and sunlit and from the shallow waters of the pond, which is rimmed with the massed dead stalks of last year's cattails, and from the small inlet filled with rush-covered tussocks, the sound of peepers is shrill and nearly earsplitting, as though hundreds upon hundreds of tiny high-pitched whistles were being blown. The peeper chorus seems to come from everywhere: from roadside ditches, from rain puddles, from sunny marshes, and from dark pools deep in the woods.

At the inlet we are completely surrounded by calling peepers. What do they look like? As they appear to be calling from the waters around the tussocks we too will have to go into the water if we hope to see them. The moment we step into the shallow pond the chorus stops. We remain

25

completely silent and motionless, and hope our patience will be rewarded. After a few minutes, one of the more daring frogs ventures its "peep, peep, peep," and soon another and another join in, until the entire chorus is again in full call. It is difficult to pinpoint any particular call. They seem to come from everywhere around us, and it is necessary to concentrate on one definite direction. As we slowly, gently, bend down to the tussock which seems to harbor the caller closest to us, its voice stops abruptly. Our quick search of the tussock reveals nothing. When I first began to study the spring peeper, this search could go on for hours; I would pinpoint the call, move, and the peeper would apparently put on a cloak of invisibility. It was most frustrating not to be able to find the caller, which I knew must be right at my feet.

Now, I have discovered that a high-pitched whistle on my part will entice a peeper to break its silence. I continue to bend and to whistle, and the peepers continue to answer, and shortly I am able to get my first glimpse, this year, of one of them.

Most people, when they see their first peeper, have a reaction of

An American toad entering the breeding pond.

surprise. First, that they are able to see the small creature at all as it sits partially submerged in the muddy water, hidden among the dead leaves at the base of a tussock. Second, they are amazed that such a tiny animal, barely the size of a thumbnail, is capable of producing such a loud, piercing sound.

Now that I have spotted the peeper I again stand motionless. Either it has not seen me or it has accepted me as part of its surroundings. There, on a little stalk at the base of the tussock, it sits quite unperturbed, peeping away, and, in doing so, inflates an enormous bubble under its throat. The bubble is almost as large as the peeper itself. The correct technical term for the bubble is "vocal sac," and it acts as a resonator.

Frogs usually call with their mouths and nostrils closed. Their calls are produced by pumping air back and forth between their lungs and over their vocal cords into the mouth. On the floor of the mouth are one or two internal openings, depending on whether the vocal sacs are single or paired. The air, passing into the opening, or openings, finds its way

A male American toad swells his throat into a bubble almost as large as his head.

A female American toad with two males clinging to her back.

Many paired American toads can be seen floating together. The male is much smaller than the female.

Mating position of American toads. Note two long strings of eggs being laid by the female. They are visible beneath the legs of the much smaller male.

into either the one or the two pockets formed by an extension of the mouth lining. If the skin surrounding the pocket is thin, this produces a throat bubble. The peeper is an example of a salientian with a single, external vocal sac. The wood frogs, which we saw earlier, have paired vocal sacs, one on each side of the throat. However, these are not visible when the frog calls because the skin surrounding them is thick and does not permit the formation of transparent throat bubbles.

Our peeper remains in place, blending so well with the dead grasses and leaves that we might lose it if we looked away. Very gently we bend down to obtain a closer look at the tiny creature and see on its back a large mark resembling an X, or a cross. This is an identifying field mark of the spring peeper, and accounts for its scientific name of *Hyla crucifer,* or literally, the "cross-bearing tree frog." Also visible are its large toe pads which allow the peeper, and all other hylas, to climb so surefootedly. Now, as the male continues to call, another peeper swims toward him. This one is slightly larger, a female heavy with eggs. Our male sees her and leaps into the water and onto her back. Clasping her body with his front legs he fertilizes her eggs as she lays them on submerged plants. This position of the male clasping the female, is called by scientists, "amplexus." The eggs are laid singly, and not in clusters like the wood frog's. One tiny female peeper can lay as many as one thousand eggs.

Frogs are largely creatures of the night, so we return to the pond a few days later, well after sunset. It is a cool overcast night, around 48°, but it appears to be perfect peeper weather, for the intensity of their chorus is overwhelming. The peepers are much more daring at night than during the day. They seem to be undisturbed by our presence and do not stop calling even when we flash our light over the nearest tussocks. Very shortly our beam catches a calling male, his pumping bubble reflecting the light as it expands, and looking much larger in the light than it did during the day. Literally hundreds of peepers surround us, for our roving light glints and reflects from their inflated throats as though they were pieces of glass. Their calls also have a hypnotic effect, for the concentrated shrilling has begun to numb our hearing to any other sound. Then we hear the recurring, soothing deep-voiced call of a barred owl, just arrived on a neighboring tree. The night slowly grows colder and the frog chorus gradually wanes. Even though deeply chilled, we are one experience richer.

By mid-April spring is firmly entrenched. Throughout the woods the green of skunk cabbage flames wherever there is moisture. Red-winged blackbirds chatter "o-kalee-ee-ee" in the marsh and teeter briefly on the cattails. The air is cool, but the sun is warmly bright and reflects in the brown sogginess of the earth around the pond. It is beautiful in the woods. It is also the day that has been awaited all winter. Today, hopefully, the first toads will call.

The lovely, flutelike sound comes from the pond—not a single call but a blending of many trills of various pitches. The melodious voices, echoing one another in what seems to be a paean to spring, force one to linger and listen. Considered by many to be the most beautiful of all wild calls, this is the courtship call of the American toad, *Bufo americanus*.

The water in the pond bubbles with the commotion caused by innumerable small creatures splashing in the shallows. Most people meet their first toad in a garden or a garage, or a cellar, for toads are creatures of the woods and gardens. But once a year the toads congregate in large groups in the water to begin the life cycle of a new generation. There is nothing subtle or secretive about the toads' courtship and their propagation drive is so intense that, unlike the wood frogs, they ignore one's presence completely.

Right there, not ten feet away, one of them sits on a log in the water. In an erect position, his head thrown back, his front feet determinedly planted, the male toad swells his black throat into a light bubble almost as large as his head and utters his sweet trill with an almost challenging

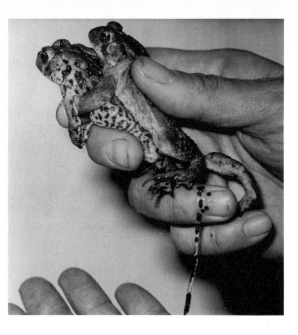

The male American toad shows no inclination to release the female from his tight grip. She has already started to lay eggs.

air. A few feet away, on a shallow sandbank, another male calls, and over there, on the top of a submerged rock, is a third. Another toad tries to clamber onto the log from which the first male calls, and is promptly thrown off.

Much has been written about the possible meaning of these calls. While, seemingly, the male seeks to attract a female, the call may also serve to delineate and establish the right to the little territory the toad occupies. A female toad, with pale throat, now arrives and is immediately approached by a male. Another male approaches and a scuffle between the two ensues. In the excitement of the mass courtship the male toads will grab and try to clasp any moving, and seemingly suitable, object. If what the toad has grabbed is another male, the latter will utter a few chirps, known as the "warning" call, and the clasping male will immediately release the other.

Egg strings of the American toad. Within the long gelatinous strings are black specks, which are the toad embryos.

A prima donna could well envy the American toad for its breath control.

A female floats calmly by with two males clinging to her back, each ignoring the other until the female submerges suddenly, dislodging one of them. The males are considerably smaller than the females, and can also be distinguished by the vocal sac, which is clearly visible, even when not inflated, as a fold of dark skin under the throat. At this time, in addition, the males develop horny nuptial pads on the thumb and inner fingers as an aid in gripping the females. A color differentiation between males and females is also obvious. Although toads are usually regarded as drab brown or gray creatures, during the courtship period the female's skin usually brightens to a light orange or even brick red color.

Amidst the calling males and swimming females many paired toads can be seen floating together. Close to our feet drifts a mating pair. As we pick them up the male shows no inclination to release the female from his tight grip. She has already started to lay eggs, which come out of her body in two long gelatinous strings. Within the strings are tiny

32

black specks, perhaps as many as 8,000, each about 1 millimeter in diameter. These are the embryos which, depending on the temperature and other conditions, will shortly emerge as tadpoles.

Very carefully we put the pair back into the water and, aside from the few chirps uttered by the male when we picked them up, they seem unconcerned by the temporary interruption of the egg-laying and fertilizing activities. As the female lays her eggs, the male deposits his sperm on them. Close to the shore, twisted around some debris on the shallow bottom of the pond, are several coils of the long egg strings, their transparency clouded by the sediment in which they lie. They are quite a bit thicker than when they were laid, for the water makes the gelatinous covering swell.

Over the years, during the toad mating season, I have frequently found dead females, some of them still in the clasp of the male. Many believe that possibly the male, clasping the female in a tight embrace for several days, might inadvertently strangle her. But scientists have discovered that the females, weakened by the mating pressure, and with their skin broken from the male's strong clasp, are more susceptible to a bacterial infection, called "redleg," which can enter a frog's or toad's body through an abrasion of the skin. I once observed an American toad tightly clasping a female for more than two weeks. The female's upper body was squeezed into a misshapen balloon, suffused red in color, and she was obviously weakening. It took much effort to force apart the

Giant toad, Bufo marinus.

The diet of the hognose snake consists primarily of toads.

male's clasping arms, which were absolutely rigid. The female, when released, was limp and the midsection was rubbed raw.

It is now nearly noon and the toad voices are in full chorus. Everywhere are males with inflated vocal sacs, uttering their mellow calls. I am always amazed at how long the American toad can hold a trill. I have timed it on many occasions and found that a call of 15 seconds duration is not unusual. Many a prima donna could well envy the toad for its breath control. Not all species of toads, however, are capable of the sustained calls of the American toad, nor are their calls of such melodious beauty.

Except for these annual courtship gatherings, toads are solitary creatures. Once their breeding season has ended, they retreat to the woods or other upland habitats. Contrary to the true frogs, whose thin, moist skin makes them vulnerable to dehydration, the toads' dry, rough skin permits them to live away from water, except for an occasional necessary soak, for which even a puddle will do. Like most amphibians, they do not drink water, but absorb it through their skin.

Toads are widely distributed throughout the American continents, from the western toad, *Bufo boreas,* which lives as far north as Alaska, to the many species in South America, including the giant toad, *Bufo marinus,* which lives southward to Patagonia. In size, also, they vary greatly. The North American Colorado River toad, *Bufo alvarius,* and the giant toad both may reach a length of 7 inches, but the oak toad, *Bufo quercicus* of the southern United States averages only one inch.

Despite their differences in size, toads look so much alike that even a casual observer can easily recognize them. Their most typical characteristics are the warts on their skin and, more notably, the two paratoid glands on the head behind the eyes. It is of these eyes that Shakespeare wrote that the toad "wears yet a precious jewel in his head," and they are truly deserving of the poetry they have inspired. The large oval pupil is black and surrounded by a golden iris and the eyes sparkle with alertness and curiosity.

There is absolutely no truth to the superstition that toads give warts to people. This belief probably started because toads do exude from their skin glands poisons which bear such names as bufotalin, bufonin, and bufogin to denote their origin. Although these poisons are harmless to humans, except if brought into contact with the eyes or mucous membrane, many a dog which has seized a *Bufo marinus,* or giant toad, has not lived long enough to learn its lesson. Even mouthing a small toad can convince a dog or other mammal that toads are not for eating.

I once watched a large bullfrog grab a small toad which was hopping through the pondside rushes. As soon as the toad was swallowed it was spat out again most emphatically, and the bullfrog spent the next few minutes with its mouth hanging open, as though trying to get air. It was apparently suffering great discomfort.

One animal, however, that appears to be immune to the toad's toxicity is the hognose snake. In addition to being able to thrive on a diet which consists in large part of toads, it has other unusual habits. When the snake believes itself to be in danger it will put on a frightening act of ferocity. Flattening and spreading its head so that it looks like a cobra, the snake will thurst its head forward repeatedly, meanwhile hissing loudly. If this act fails to frighten the observer, the snake will suddenly

One mammal that seems fond of eating toads is the striped skunk. (Michigan Department of Conservation)

The red-tailed hawk preys on toads. (Michigan Department of Conservation)

appear to weaken, gasp feebly, roll over on its back, shudder a bit, and "die." The hognose snake has one of the best "play-dead" acts in all the animal world. Actually, it is completely harmless except to toads. One mammal that does seem to be fond of toads is the skunk, and many birds, such as crows and various species of hawks, also prey on toads.

More than just size differentiates the various species of toads, and trying to identify them by size alone can lead to incorrect results. Color, too, can be misleading, for many species occur in a wide range of color variations. What mainly guides herpetologists (those who specialize in the study of amphibians and reptiles) in identification are such characteristics as the size and shape of a toad's paratoid glands, the appearance of its cranial knobs, whether or not there is a raised area (a boss) between the eyes, the pattern of the warts, and, of course, the general shape and appearance of the animal.

The character of the warts, for example, is one of the principal distinguishing factors between the two species of toads in the eastern United States—the American toad and the Fowler's toad. The American toad has only one or two large warts in each of the dark spots on its back; Fowler's toad has three or more small warts. While this may seem to be an unimportant detail, the difference between the two species becomes even more obvious when they call. Fowler's toad has none of the American toad's beautiful long melodious trill, instead it issues a short and nasal bleat.

Farther south, particularly in Florida, the American toad is replaced by the southern toad, *Bufo terrestris*. As a general rule American and southern toads will not be found in the same region, but Fowler's toad overlaps both of their ranges. Where both species exist, interbreeding does, on occasion, occur, but this is comparatively rare, due primarily to their different breeding periods. The American toad breeds from late March through July, whereas Fowler's toad rarely commences its activities until after the American toad has left the breeding waters.

A toad is an avid eater, feeding mainly on insects and worms. Its estimated capacity for devouring several thousand insects a month makes it a valuable animal in pest control. Voracious as it is, however, a toad will never eat anything that doesn't move. Since a toad is fairly near-

The American toad has only one or two large warts in each of the dark spots on its back.

Fowler's toad has three or more small warts in each of the dark spots on its back.

With incredible speed the American toad whips out its tongue.

sighted it will not start to stalk an insect, or other moving object, until the prey is almost within tongue-snapping range. If the insect should stop moving, the toad will freeze, become absolutely motionless, and there will develop what appears to be a game of endurance between the two, for the toad will not move until the insect does. Then, with incredible speed, the toad whips out its tongue, which is fastened to the front of its lower jaw and is loose at the back. The insect, captured by the toad's sticky tongue, is flicked back into the toad's mouth. As the toad swallows, it closes its eyes. This brings the eyes pressing down into the upper part of the toad's mouth, and assists in pushing the food down its throat.

Frequently the sticky tongue picks up not only the insect but surrounding dirt, dried leaves, and miscellaneous debris as well. When this is repugnant to the toad it will use its front feet as hands to forcibly thrust the unpleasant matter from its mouth. The front feet are also used in this manner when larger prey, such as earthworms, cannot be swallowed in one gulp. The toad stuffs the reluctant and struggling animal into its mouth, frequently changing the position of its "hands" in order to obtain a better grip, and continues stuffing and swallowing until, with one last large gulp, the worm completely disappears.

38

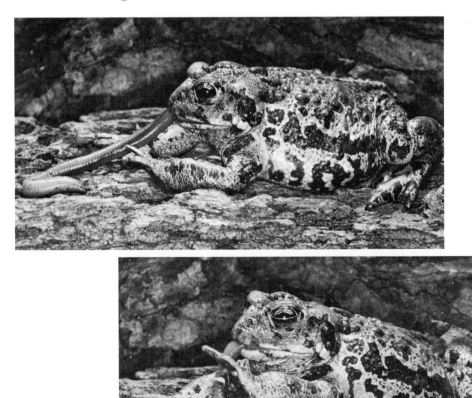

Western toad eating an earthworm. Note how the toad uses its "hands" to get a better grip.

While primarily used for feeding, the toad's tongue also serves as a means of attack. This can be observed whenever a group of captive toads is fed together. If one toad goes after the food more energetically than the others they will frequently turn from the dish and throw their tongues, with the attendant snapping sound, at that toad instead of at the food. Although some observers maintain that the toads believe the culprit's moving tongue is probably a flying insect, and thus a suitable morsel, I have noticed that they will sometimes suddenly renew the attack at a later period, even if the toad is sitting quietly at the time. When attacked in this manner the victim will frequently snap its tongue at its tormentors in return.

When a toad is faced with a real danger, however, its reaction is entirely different. It will inflate its body with air, making itself appear much larger, or it will bow its head forward, thus forming its body into a crouched ball. At one time I had an opportunity to observe the reaction of a group of toads into whose midst I introduced their traditional enemy, a hognose snake. There was no dillydallying then with tongue-snapping or defense positions. Each toad immediately went into what, in humans, would be called hysterics, began to leap wildly about, and within a very few minutes all had turned a pale ghostlike beige in color, a perfect example of turning pale with fear.

Another visit to the pond a few days later reveals that most of the toads have left, returned to their solitary life on land. The water is just as crowded, however, although much quieter. The gelatinous egg strings still twist and cluster in the shallows, but with a difference. A few, now hanging limply straight, contain small white beads. These are eggs that will never develop, but will gradually disintegrate. Most of the rest of the strings are thin and torn and drift lazily in the slight movement of the wind-driven water.

The pond debris is now streaked with thousands upon thousands of

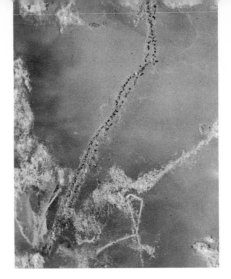

The embryos in the disintegrating egg strings of the American toad resemble short brush strokes when they begin to develop.

tiny creatures that hang from the torn egg strings, roots, weeds, and any other clingable object. Only a few millimeters in length and resembling short, straight brush strokes, these are the tadpoles that have just hatched from the toads' eggs. For a short time these tiny animals hang quietly, twitching their tails or swimming very short distances only when they are disturbed. But within a few days they will begin to grow and to transform, and the pond bottom will flash and teem with the twirling, giddy trips of the small creatures, each of which resembles an inkblack buckshot with a tail.

The word "tadpole," by which the larval toads and frogs are known, comes from medieval English, *tadd* or *tade* meaning "toad," and *poll* meaning "head"—a toad that is all head. Probably no part of the toad's or frog's life holds as much fascination for us as does the metamorphosis which these creatures undergo.

Metamorphosis is, of course, not characteristic of the frogs and toads

The pond bottom is enlivened by the darting movements of the small black creatures which are the tadpoles of the American toad.

Very young American toad tadpoles—greatly enlarged.

alone. A great many creatures, including insects and man, undergo changes in form and structure. However, these changes usually take place within the egg or the womb, and when these creatures, other than certain insects, have emerged, they bear a definite resemblance to their parents. With very few exceptions, however, the offspring of the frogs and toads, upon emerging from the egg, differ so markedly from the adult in appearance and structure that no one could possibly guess that they were the same animal.

In the metamorphosis of beetles, butterflies, moths, and other orders of insects, a similar morphological change can be found. The adult insect lays an egg from which a larva, wormlike in appearance, emerges. When the larva is full-grown it turns into what appears to be a lifeless object, the pupa. Inside the pupa, behind closed doors so to speak, a process takes place which is tantamount to a breakdown and reconstruction of the animal's organs. When this is completed, the pupa breaks open and from it emerges the new creature.

Not so with the frogs and toads. There, to our great pleasure, we can observe, day by day, the changes that take place until the entire process of transformation is complete. Closer observation will reveal that the tadpole does not have protruding eyes, a characteristic so typical of the adult, nor does it have the adult's wide mouth. Instead the tadpole has a round mouth which contains horny mandibles or sometimes teeth, designed to scrape its food from the rocks and plants. Voracious eaters, the tadpoles feed primarily on algae and aquatic plant life, but they also eat animal matter and occasionally turn cannibalistic. I have watched them form large, amorphous groups, all attempting to gnaw on what appeared to be a blueberry, but was actually a dead tadpole. Whether they had killed one of their own kind or were simply scavenging, I was not able to determine.

The shape of a tadpole's mouth, and the arrangement of the teeth, if any, is one of the means used by herpetologists for species identification. At a quick glance identification is usually extremely difficult. Although size depends not only on the species but on the age of the animal as well, tadpoles of the true frogs (Ranidae) are generally larger in relation to the adults than are the tadpoles of the true toads (Bufonidae). The bull-frog tadpole may attain the relatively great length of more than six inches. Shapes also vary. Toad tadpoles, as we have seen, are round and black, while frog tadpoles are, as a rule, oval in form, lighter in color and frequently speckled. The tail of a toad tadpole is thin, almost stringlike, while the tails of the tadpoles of many frogs are broad and frequently colorful, like a flowing, waving fan.

As the toad tadpole grows older, the hind legs appear.

As the tadpole grows older, the hind legs appear and the front legs start to develop beneath the skin. Gradually other changes take place. The tail shrinks as the tadpole stops eating and obtains its nourishment by absorbing its tail. At the same time the tadpole assumes more and more the appearance of the adult. The head takes shape as the mouth broadens and the eyes develop lids and begin to protrude. Internally, too, there are radical changes as the gills disappear and the lungs take over the function of breathing. The intestines shorten to adapt from a vegetarian diet to a diet of insects and other small live animals. Soon the tadpole is ready to start life on land as a toad. The tail is the last tadpole characteristic to disappear. The half-tadpole–half-adult continues to take nourishment from the tail until it is completely absorbed. The time taken by a tadpole to become an adult varies, depending primarily on the species but often also on the environment.

Despite the enormous number of tadpoles that hatch, very few of them reach maturity. The tiny creatures are food for many water-living and land animals. Crayfishes, water beetles, dragonfly nymphs and other animals feed on them. I once observed several newts sitting in the midst of a mass of tadpoles gorging themselves, sweeping the creatures within

Contrary to the tadpoles, the larvae of salamanders more or less resemble the adults.

Red-spotted newt.

reach by means of their tails, and devouring tadpole after tadpole. Disease, too, takes its toll. This is, after all, nature's way of keeping a check on overpopulation. Since each female toad lays thousands of eggs, natural predation, or control of their numbers, is important. There is, however, another enemy of water creatures, man-made and very deadly. This is water pollution. Toads are not selective breeders, and during their courtship period they are apt to congregate anywhere there is quiet water. The resultant tadpoles swarm in drainage ditches and excavation pits. I once found a tremendous congregation in a shallow pit, formed by a torrential storm, in soft clay left by some builders. Many of these bodies of water are badly polluted by chemicals and industrial wastes. The parent toads obviously don't know any better, and the eggs simply have no chance to develop.

Barely a hundred miles from New York City, and less than half that distance from Philadelphia, lies one of the unique natural regions of the country, the Pine Barrens of New Jersey. The area encompasses some 1,300,000 acres, of which roughly 100,000 acres is contained in the Wharton Tract, a recreational area owned by the State of New Jersey.

45

Sandy, sinkable paths and roads crisscross stretches of land studded with stunted pitch pine and small, broken oak trees or lead suddenly into vast marshes that are abandoned cranberry bogs.

At first visit the name Pine Barrens might seem justified, but closer exploration reveals that the area is a naturalist's happy hunting ground. Rare plants grow abundantly and it is interesting to note that various plant life zones seem to meet there. This southern area of New Jersey is the northernmost limit of the southern yellow orchid and of approximately 160 other southern plants, while the bearberry and about 80 other northern plants are probably not found any farther south. The region's best known plant is the tiny and inconspicuous curly grass fern, an attraction for botanists from all over the world. Pink and white lady's slippers, bog asphodel, pitcher plants, sundews, pixie moss, and a host of other plants are all to be found in this so-called barren land, which abounds with bogs, streams and swamps. The dark, rust-colored water of the acrid cedar bogs is one of the outstanding characteristics of the region. It is these bogs that provide habitat and breeding pools for two species of frogs, one of which, the carpenter frog, has a very limited range outside the Barrens, and the other, the Pine Barrens tree frog, is virtually unknown anywhere else.

The carpenter frog of the Atlantic coastal plain has a loud hammerlike call.

Northern cricket frog.

The carpenter frog or sphagnum frog, *Rana virgatipes,* lives up to both of its vernacular names. Found frequently in the sphagnum bogs of the Pine Barrens, its range is limited to the Atlantic coastal plains. About 2 to 2½ inches long the frog somehow gives the impression of being larger. Although the four light stripes on its body serve as positive identification, its over-all drab body is well camouflaged in the dark waters of the Barrens. As a result it is very difficult to find. Each note of its call sounds like a short, rapid hammer stroke, and during the breeding season, April through August, the echoing "hammerblows" can be heard throughout the swamps and bogs where these frogs live and breed. This call has given it the name of carpenter frog.

The other rare frog found in the Pine Barrens is so closely connected with the region that it is called the Pine Barrens tree frog. Previously called Anderson's tree frog because of its first discovery near Anderson, South Carolina, it still retains the scientific name of *Hyla andersoni.* Today, however, except for a few isolated colonies in North Carolina and Georgia it lives only in the Pine Barrens. Barely more than an inch and a half in length, its back is a light emerald green. A lavender stripe, bordered with white, outlines its sides, and its bright orange inner thighs, spotted with yellow, make it one of the world's most beautiful frogs.

I was most fortunate in meeting Jim Starkey, head of the Science Department of the Vineland, New Jersey, High School, and an ardent field naturalist with a special interest in amphibia. Born and raised near the

Pine Barrens, he knows the region intimately and when I expressed a wish to see a *Hyla andersoni* he invited me to come to Vineland, saying, "I can guarantee you one."

The best time for any frog safari is, of course, at night during the breeding season, so in May I arrived at Vineland and eagerly reported in. We packed our gear into Jim's Jeep and went off to the Wharton Tract where Jim drove casually over the narrow trails of soft, clinging sand which are a trap for the unsuspecting driver. Abruptly he pulled over to the side, and turned off the lights and the motor. We both remained completely silent.

The night was clear and the air was comfortably warm. I could hear the bleating of Fowler's toads not far away, and from all around us came the call of whippoorwills. Suddenly there was a sound like the distant quacking of a large flock of ducks. I had heard that sound before, on a record issued by Cornell University Press, called "Voices of the Night," and I immediately recognized it as the call of *Hyla andersoni*.

We left the car, burdened with boots, flashlights and camera, and proceeded to follow the calls. They drew us to the edge of a swampy pond, its banks thickly overgrown with blueberry bushes and scrubby pines. The moon was glimmering on the water, and the final, fairy-tale, effect was accomplished by the incessant almost-hypnotic calls and the zooming flight of innumerable whippoorwills. The exuberant bird cries partially deafened us to the intermixed calls of what must have been hundreds of *Hyla andersoni*. Jim and I tried to pinpoint the call of one specific frog. The best way to locate a single caller is by triangulation, so Jim directed his flashlight to one point, and I did the same from another angle. Slowly and quietly we closed in so as not to disturb the caller, moving when we heard its "quank-quank-quank" and stopping when it fell silent.

Suddenly Jim pointed his flashlight toward a blueberry bush. There was a *Hyla andersoni,* blending so perfectly into the leaves that I would

The Pine Barrens tree frog. One of the world's most beautiful frogs.

never have discovered it without Jim's light pointer. It had stopped calling, apparently sensing danger, but its vocal sac was still inflated. It appeared to me to be even more beautiful than in its pictures. The delicate little creature, flatter than most frogs, reminded me of an oriental "fingering" piece, those small jade objects held for peace and relaxation.

We continued to find more callers, and I even managed to keep one under observation while it called. As with so many small hylids, the intensity of the sound produced is entirely out of proportion to the size of the frog. The little creature kept pumping air from its lungs into the inflated sac which, with each air intake, grew ever more inflated. All the frogs we found were males. The females, being voiceless, can be discovered only by chance. We carefully scanned the swamp hoping to find a female or a mating pair, but all in vain.

After we had finished exploring that particular swamp we went on to others in the vicinity. From everywhere the Pine Barrens tree frogs called in ever-increasing intensity. If one were to estimate their numbers from the multivoiced clamor it would be impossible to come to the conclusion that this tree frog is a threatened species. Unfortunately, it is unquestionably in danger of extinction.

Hyla andersoni has chosen for its habitat a region of rather unique ecological make-up, and apparently requires for its own reproduction the acid bogs and cedar swamps found in the Pine Barrens. Its location in central New Jersey puts this frog in a very precarious survival position, for the two-pronged attack of urban and industrial expansion reaches ever closer to this island of wilderness. There is presently a hope that some part of the Pine Barrens may be set aside as a National Monument. If this should materialize it would be a very important step in our effort to save some of our country's natural beauty and resources. It is up to us, collectively, to determine whether this beautiful little animal will be seen only as a lifeless, faded specimen preserved in formaldehyde; to determine whether the curly grass fern and a host of other plants will become only crumbling, pressed specimens of interest only to the natural historian. Wouldn't it be ironic, as well as tragic, if the day should come when most of nature's beauty could be studied only as history, as a thing of the past.

One evening my friend, Jim Starkey, detoured in order to introduce me to a pond surrounded by what had once been farmland and was now being thoughtlessly "improved" out of existence by a town. Farm ponds are usually hosts to innumerable aquatic creatures, and I was curious to find out what was resident there. What greeted me was the sound, apparently, of thousands of small pebbles being clicked together. Although this sound did not have the carrying power of the high-pitched call of the spring peeper it was, nevertheless, impressive.

On the bank of the pond I tried to pinpoint a particular producer of this rather unique call. One seemed to be calling almost at my feet, like the clicking of two pebbles. It was awesome to try to estimate how many thousands of the small callers must be in the pond to create a noise of such over-all intensity, when each individual call was so thin. The callers were the northern cricket frog, *Acris crepitans crepitans.*

With some skill, patience, and a good flashlight it did not take long to see one of these tiny creatures, no larger than a spring peeper but somewhat slimmer. Unlike the peeper, the cricket frog calls in the open and is therefore much easier to find, as the light picks up its greatly inflated single vocal sac. Catching a cricket frog, however, is a difficult feat. In relation to its size *Acris crepitans* is the jumping champion of the frog world, the "salientissimus" of the salientians. What makes pursuing or capturing it so difficult is not only its long-distance leaps but also its jumping speed and particularly the zigzag pattern of its flight. We were very lucky to catch one. The likeness of the cricket frog to the spring

*Eastern spadefoot toad.
Note the vertical pupil of its
eye as reflected in the
flashlight beam.*

peeper is only in its size. The skin of the cricket frog is grainy, or warty. This skin texture, the dark triangle on the back of its head, and the absence of well-developed toe pads are its best identification marks, but differentiation between the various species of cricket frogs and their close relatives the chorus frogs (genus Pseudacris) can be very difficult and tricky, for their coloring and patterns are highly variable.

In New York State the northern cricket frog is reputedly limited to Long Island. However, in April of 1963, while peeper hunting in Westchester County I heard the familiar clicking call, and spent the rest of the day trying to disprove my ears. After several hours of swamp wading I finally found a small colony of cricket frogs, which I was able to observe before they further proved their identity by zigzagging away. For the past three springs I have revisited the area to see whether these pioneers have been able to establish themselves in this outlying land. Although they were still there in the spring of 1966, I am not confident about their future, for the colony has apparently not increased.

A few nights after our May expedition to find the Pine Barrens tree frog, Jim and I were returning from one of our trips to the Pine Barrens. It was raining, one of those heavy spring rains on which so much of life depends. Suddenly, in the beam of the headlights, we saw a myriad of small, glittering, gleaming flashes. It looked as though tiny pieces of

A clean spadefoot toad looks like a ceramic figurine.

Young spadefoot toads.

metal or glass had been strewn on the road, and were reflecting our lights. Jim stopped the car, and it became apparent that the objects were moving in a mass across the road. We immediately jumped out and, reflected in our flashlight beams, were the same golden gleams. These came from the eyes of the eastern spadefoot toad, *Scaphiopus holbrooki,* a creature seldom seen, for it spends most of its life underground and almost never comes to the surface during the day. During their breeding seasons, however, apparently stimulated by a warm spring rain, they emerge from the ground in great numbers, and travel to the breeding pools. It was this event that Jim had brought me to see.

I picked up one of the toads for a closer look. Its outstanding feature is its eyes, which appear to be even more prominent than those of other frogs and toads. The iris is golden, not yellow but molten metallic gold, and the pupils are vertical, an identification mark of the family Pelobatidae to which the spadefoot toad belongs. With the exception of the spadefoot and *Ascaphus truei,* the tailed frog of the Pacific Northwest, all frogs and toads in the United States have either round or horizontal pupils.

In its general appearance a spadefoot toad resembles a small true toad of the genus Bufo. It has the same over-all compact shape, and the paratoid glands, although small and round, may be present. However, the spadefoot's skin, though warty, is smooth, and under the layer of dirt

53

which usually covers it, it has beautiful coloring and design. It is commonly olive or dark brown with an irregular yellow linear pattern superimposed. A clean spadefoot toad looks more like a ceramic figurine than a living creature. What gives the spadefoot its name is a horny black tubercle on the inside of its hind feet. The size and shape of the tubercle is helpful in identifying the species.

Spadefoot toads are massive breeders. Many of them, as they cross the highways on their way to the breeding pools, fall victim to automobiles. Although we had pulled our car off the road, many other cars zoomed by and crushed dozens of the migrants. As with most traveling amphibia, first come the males. With enormously inflated single external vocal sacs they utter their eerie crowlike calls. A large spadefoot chorus may, on a clear night, be heard a mile away. Their courtship behavior is very similar to that of the other mass-breeding frogs and toads. After a few nights it is over, and all that remains are the eggs, which are laid in irregular bands on stalks of plants near the surface of the water. After the egg laying is finished the spadefoot toad resumes its solitary life as a denizen of the underground.

The tubercle, or "spade," on its hind feet enables the spadefoot to dig itself into the ground with astonishing rapidity. The instinctive reaction to dig itself in can be easily observed by placing a spadefoot on the palm

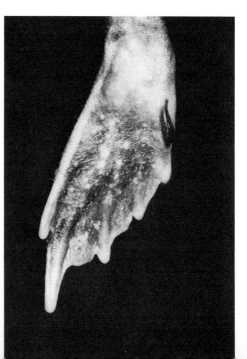

Foot of spadefoot toad, showing "spade."

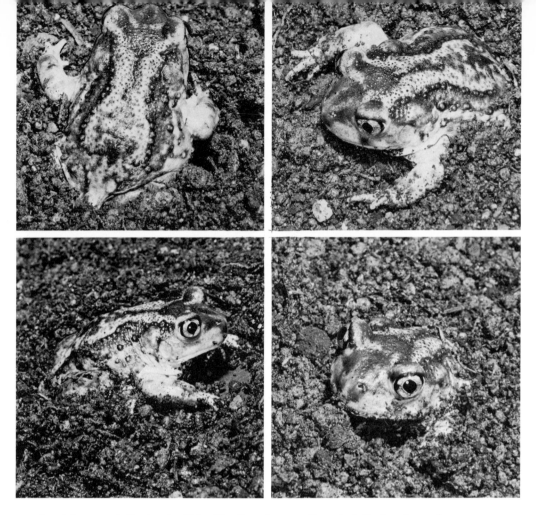

Spadefoot toad digging itself in. Finally only a small part of the head remains above ground, displaying the golden eye even more prominently.

of your hand. Immediately the hind feet begin to scratch and its body starts to rock backward, trying to escape not, as is usual, by jumping away but by digging. Place a spadefoot on top of some loose earth and it will immediately start its backward digging process and, in so doing, will often turn round and round, looking for all the world as though it were screwing itself into the ground. The hindlegs disappear first, then the body, and after a few minutes only a small part of the head remains above ground, displaying the golden eyes even more prominently. Then a few more quick motions, and the toad has completely disappeared. There may be a small telltale mound which will soon collapse, leaving no trace of the animal whatsoever.

55

The eastern spadefoot, though rarely seen outside of the breeding season, does emerge frequently on rainy nights to eat worms, beetles, crickets, spiders, and the like. On these occasions the toads are voracious feeders, for their meal periods may be few and far between. Owing to their underground habits not much is known about their lives. We do know that while the spadefoot is underground its metabolism is slowed down considerably, and it breathes through its skin. A dug-up spadefoot has the listless or sleepy appearance of a creature found in hibernation.

The eastern spadefoot, though it lives in wooded areas, prefers loose or sandy soil, such as that of the Pine Barrens. In arid parts of the United States, where other species, such as Couch's spadefoot, the western spadefoot, and others live, the very survival of the creature depends on its ability to live underground. The spadefoot does not differ from other amphibia—frogs, toads, and salamanders—in its dependence on water. When necessary it will dig ten to twelve feet below the surface to find moisture, which it absorbs through its skin. Water is also stored in its urinary bladder. This ability to find and to store water makes the spadefoot toad one of the few amphibia equipped for life in dry regions. During periods of continued drought a spadefoot may remain underground for weeks or even months.

In these arid regions the aquatic stage of an amphibian has to be short and transformation rapid, for rainfall is rare. Sporadic flash floods create temporary puddles where the frogs and toads of the area must breed, and they must breed fast if there is to be a next generation. The period of hatching time and metamorphosis depends to a great degree on the temperature. The rain pools of the Southwest may be so warm that no northern tadpole could survive in them, but the heat speeds up the hatching process and may reduce it at times to only 30 hours after fertilization.

Hurter's spadefoot, *Scaphiopus hurteri,* appears to be the high-speed champion, for Arthur N. Bragg records, in *The Natural History of*

Spring

North American Amphibians and Reptiles by James A. Oliver, an observation of 13 days from egg laying to completed metamorphosis.

The heat that warms the water also, unfortunately, evaporates it fast. Much too frequently the pool has dried before metamorphosis is complete, leaving thousands and thousands of tadpoles to die. However, if all do not metamorphize quickly enough to escape from the drying pool, many will manage to do so. As with all prolific creatures the survival of the species lies in its numbers. It is this adaptation and selection that keeps populations both alive and in check.

The tadpoles of the northeastern frogs and toads may not be confronted as frequently with the danger of fast-drying pools, but the creatures that prey upon them are much more numerous than they are in the arid regions. Diving beetles, dragonfly nymphs and other predatory insects are not likely to be found in the temporary rain pools of the desert, but they decimate the ranks of the tadpoles in the temperate and subtropical zones.

It is late spring in the Northeast. Dusk is falling as we enter the edge of the woods; the creatures of the day are ceasing their activities and

Predaceous diving beetle also preys upon tadpoles. It is usually found suspended head downward in the water with the rear end of the body, which has two large breeding pores, protruding above the surface of the water. The white spots on the beetle are small bubbles of air.

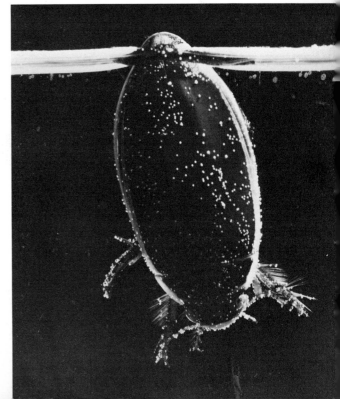

starting to settle down for the night. Suddenly the evening hush is shattered by a call suggestive of that of a woodpecker. There is a series of short, harsh trills, each lasting only a few seconds, then, after a short pause, the series starts again. The caller is the gray tree frog, *Hyla versicolor,* the only large tree frog living in the northeastern United States, and the only one in the region that is familiarly called "tree frog," for the tiny spring peeper lives in trees only a part of the year.

As the scientific name *versicolor* implies, the gray tree frog is a master of camouflage, and when calling from the crotch of a tree it can blend so perfectly with the color of the branches that it is almost impossible to see except by chance. I have seen *Hyla versicolor* in or near crevices of stone walls, on trunks of trees, on fences, and in the cracks of a busy swimming pool, and always I marvel at the frog's protective coloration. Its rough and grainy skin, together with its chunky shape, has earned it the alternate name of "tree toad." It is usually gray with a darker blotch, shaped like a Rorschach ink-blot design on its back, but the consistency of the skin, as well as the color, is extremely variable. It may be dry and shiny like a small highly varnished gourd, or it may be

Gray tree frog. One of the best camouflaged of all frogs.

Neatly tucked up in a tree, the gray tree frog looks like a small excrescence of bark.

moist and slippery. It may be pearly gray or almost white and it may become drab dark gray, brown or olive.

Color changes are not, of course, limited to *Hyla versicolor*. Almost all tree frogs, and many other frogs and toads, are subject to a wide range of color changes—dark or light—caused by the change in the shape of the pigment cells. Such changes may be brought on by various stimuli to the tree frog, both external and internal. Low temperatures cause its pigment to expand and its skin to assume a dark color but high temperatures produce the opposite effect. Bright light, incident as well as reflected, will cause the skin to turn pale, while subdued light or darkness causes the color to darken.

Curiously, however, color changes are influenced as greatly by the surface texture of the frog's surroundings, thus contact with a rough object will tend to darken the skin, while a smooth surface will cause it to lighten. Various chemicals and the degree of moisture in the skin also serve as stimuli for color changes, as does, apparently, nervous tension, exemplified by the toads that were visited by the hognose snake. This changeable color extends over the tree frog's back but the belly remains white, as does the small spot beneath each eye. Serving as an identification mark, *Hyla versicolor* alone among tree frogs of similar appearance has orange inner thighs. A simple method of telling the sexes apart is the presence of the dark fold on the throat of the male *versicolor*. This is the vocal sac which, when not inflated, is tucked neatly away beneath the chin, as it is with all male frogs and toads with a single external vocal sac.

59

Grasshopper. A delicacy to many frogs.

In common with all other members of the genus Hyla, *versicolor* also has adhesive disks on the tips of its toes, but when the frog is relaxed these are not immediately apparent, for in repose it tucks its forearms under its chest and keeps the hind legs close to the body. When disturbed, however, it can climb with great rapidity or leap with agility, as many a winged insect has discovered when it became part of a tree frog's meal.

Hyla versicolor, like many other species of frogs, has a strong sense of location. For many years I had a tall glass-sided case in which lived five gray tree frogs of various ages, all of which could usually be found in the same places on the same branches. When it occasionally became necessary to take the frogs out of the case I soon found that no matter where they were placed when I returned them, the frogs would, within minutes, be tucked up, arms under their chest, in their habitual locations. In the wild also, *Hyla versicolor* rarely wanders far from its chosen perch on a branch or in the crotch of a tree. There, thanks to its near-perfect camouflage, it is well concealed from both predator and prey. As an insect approaches, the frog, attracted by the moving object, snatches and devours it. I have observed gray tree frogs eat quite large insects, such as katydids and grasshoppers, seemingly unconcerned by

60

The gray tree frog feeds on grasshoppers and is seemingly unconcerned by their long and spiny legs.

the insect's long and spiny legs. The actual process of swallowing the food may take some time and it is a grotesque sight to see the victim's rear end and legs sticking out of the frog's mouth while the frog tries to stuff the morsel down its throat with its forefeet, or "hands."

Hyla versicolor may be regarded as one of the least shy of the frogs. This makes it an excellent subject for observation, for, unless physically disturbed or startled, it will remain calmly folded in place, may consent to accept food from your hand, and will go on with its normal occupations as though you were not there. In this way you may, with luck, watch the frog call.

As *Hyla versicolor* inflates its single vocal sac and utters its short, harsh trills its entire little body vibrates like that of a riveter. While most frog calls are uttered in connection with courtship and breeding activities there are other factors which may induce a frog to start calling

—their voices can frequently be heard before a thunderstorm or during rain. I have often heard previously torpid bullfrogs react loudly to the drone of an airplane, and some tree frogs are even more easily stimulated by sounds. At one time I had a collection of several tree frogs of various species, ranging vocally from an extremely loquacious green tree frog, *Hyla cinerea,* to a quiet Pine Woods tree frog, *Hyla femoralis.* However, I had only to play a recording of frog calls to start them all calling. As each section of the record, devoted to the calls of one species of frog, would play, my frog of the same species would answer, tentatively at first, then more and more determinedly. Amusing was the reaction of that same green tree frog to other sounds. Whenever my wife spoke animatedly in conversation, or read aloud, the frog would call loudly as long as she spoke, and would increase the speed of its calls if my wife raised the pitch of her voice. We tested this frog with various other sounds and found that it reacted to a light, high-pitched female voice and to rhythmic music.

During the breeding season the gray tree frog, like all frogs, is at its most active. It is then that it descends from a tree or shrub to take up temporary residence near a shallow body of water. The males, squatting along the shore of their shallow breeding pool, their vocal sacs inflated and uttering their deafening call, are almost completely oblivious to everything around them. It is easy to approach one of them at this time. Nothing, not even being stroked gently with a stick, can distract them from their single-minded purpose, to procreate a new generation of *Hyla versicolor.*

The females, apparently attracted by the calls of the males, swim toward them and the frogs pair off. The female lays as many as 1,800 eggs in small clusters, consisting of 30 to 40 eggs each, which are usually attached to submerged leaves or blades of grass. After four or five days the tadpoles emerge from the eggs and transform, within a month and a half to two months, into tiny froglets which bear very little resemblance to their parents. It is at this stage that identification is most difficult, especially in regions where other hylids occur.

The newly transformed gray tree frogs are beautiful little creatures. Bright green in color, they look like small pieces of carved emerald, a treasure for anyone's jewel box. It must be regretted that within a month or so they will begin to put on the neat Puritan gray and white of the adults. Within a short time the small white spots beneath the eyes begin to appear, faint markings can be seen on the back, and, although the inner thighs may not turn orange until the next season, they are to all appearances miniature gray tree frogs.

It was a gray and chilly day in late March when my wife and I started to drive south. The southeastern states harbor a greater concentration of frogs and toads than anywhere else in the United States and I had long wanted to find them and study them. When we left New York there were still a few snow flurries in the air, but by the time we ended the day near Chesapeake Bay, spring was close at hand. A short evening stroll from our motel took us to a shallow pond in a nearby grove, where we were greeted by a strong peeper chorus intermixed with the calls of northern cricket frogs. We listened with pleasure, but did no exploring, for we knew that most of the new species of frogs and toads we met on our trip would continue with us at least as far as northern Florida.

Chesapeake Bay is something of a dividing line in the distribution of North American frogs and toads, and represents the northernmost range of many of the typical southern frogs. The only frog found exclusively in that region is the northern green tree frog, *Hyla cinerea evittata,* a subspecies of *Hyla cinerea,* the green tree frog. As much as we wanted to find *evittata* we did not have the time to do so and early next morning we continued south.

From then on each day's journey carried us farther and farther into spring. Each evening's stop brought a more intense frog chorus, with new voices continually added, as in a multivoiced fugue, and old ones with-

63

The limpkin, a large brown wading bird, has found a refuge on the Wakulla River.

drawn. Shortly the northern cricket frog, *Acris crepitans*, was replaced by the southern cricket frog, *Acris gryllus gryllus*, which is similar in appearance but with longer legs.

In addition to the frogs, other changes in the surroundings left little doubt that we were deep in the South. Spanish moss draped the trees, birds were everywhere, and every roadside restaurant offered hominy grits and hush puppies. Near the Georgia-Florida border we turned west toward Tallahassee and the nearby Wakulla River region which encompasses much wild swampland.

Falling asleep on the night we arrived at the hotel which was to be our headquarters was not easy. We were stimulated by the prospect of all the new frogs and toads we would, hopefully, soon see and by the exciting habitat that surrounded us. Also, the warm spring was saturated with the plaintive cry of the limpkins, hauntingly like the scream of a child in distress. Listening to the large number of these brown, long-legged rail-like birds calling out there in the dark along the river made me feel a part of the wilderness, as does the call of the loon on the isolated and remote lakes of the Far North.

Spring

The limpkin's future has become precarious, as has that of almost all nonadaptable creatures. It feeds almost exclusively on a fresh-water snail of the Southeast, the green snail, which is endangered by the ever-decreasing water level in Florida. In addition, civilization has encroached heavily on the limpkin's habitat by draining and filling in much of the swampland. Here, along the Wakulla River, the limpkin has found a haven, and has furnished an alternate name for the river, which is also known as The River of the Crying Bird.

I was fortunate in being able to enlist the help of a local wildlife warden, and next morning we embarked on our first trip into the swamp wilderness. Its banks studded with ancient cypresses and live oaks the river gave the impression of being in a fairy-tale jungle. The limpkins walked awkwardly across the large lily pads or stood on low branches of trees draped with Spanish moss, while anhinga birds with spread wings posed nearby. Huge alligators basked on logs in the warm spring sun and ignored us as our boat drifted by.

Large alligators bask in the sun along the Wakulla River.

Green tree frog. This frog is subject to drastic color changes and variations.

I asked our guide to stay close to the shore where I could be on the lookout for frogs. It did not take long to find one. On a large leaf growing out of the water sat a green tree frog, *Hyla cinerea*. Brilliantly green, with an almost-white stripe on each side reaching from its snout to its groin, around two inches long and of extremely slender build, this frog had all the typical field marks of its species. *Hyla cinerea,* like most tree frogs, is subject to drastic color changes and variations. I have seen dark brown and dark gray ones and had it not been for the nearly always present white or yellowish stripe on the frog's sides it would have been hard for me to make a positive identification, although probably no other tree frog is quite as slender.

If, on our trip south, we had taken time to explore the woods and the swamps that we passed we probably would have found a green tree frog much sooner, for we entered its range shortly after we crossed Chesapeake Bay, as we also entered the range of the Pine Woods tree frog, *Hyla femoralis,* the barking tree frog, *Hyla gratiosa,* and that of many other species which we hoped to find here. Our own *Hyla versicolor* remained with us, and we were just about in the region where both the northern spring peeper, *Hyla crucifer,* and the southern spring peeper, *Hyla crucifer bartramiana,* should be found. This area in northern Florida probably contains the greatest gathering of tree frogs in the

66

United States. And there are cricket frogs and chorus frogs (genus *Acris* and *Pseudacris*) and two new species of Bufo, and the narrow-mouthed toads (family Microhylidae), and even one or two ranids new to me. Wakulla seemed to be a paradise for one who likes frogs and toads and I looked forward to a rich and rewarding experience.

Away from the swamp formed by the river there is much upland. We explored this in search of the temporary swamps and ponds where frogs are most likely to breed. These breeding waters are quite similar to the ones we had visited in our northeastern woods if we ignore the surrounding plant life. Cypress trees, heavily draped with Spanish moss grow in the waters, each tree encircled, as though in a family group, by the gnomic cypress knees. We selected one specific pond and decided to make it our headquarters for the evening. We were guided to it after dark by the calls of what must have been thousands of frogs, and which, as we drew closer, I was afraid would become literally ear-piercing. The most prominent and ubiquitous call was a rasping sound, reminiscent of a stick run over a picket fence. Intermixed with this were chirpings, peepings, quonkings, trills and other notes. To separate and identify the various species by ear is not an easy task, and requires much field experience. I decided that the majority of the callers were cricket frogs and chorus frogs. The cricket frogs were *Acris gryllus,* which we had met earlier on our trip, and because of this frog's habit of calling "in the open" we had no trouble in sighting several of them promptly.

One call in particular attracted us. It was a peculiar sound and, in my opinion, is best described by Roger Conant in his *Field Guide to Reptiles and Amphibians* as "the sound of a rachet but with a musical quality." This was the call of the southern chorus frog, *Pseudacris nigrita nigrita.*

Since chorus frogs are very furtive we knew that it would be quite difficult to see one. Eventually we managed to catch the reflection of our flashlight in an inflated vocal sac and there was a *nigrita* in the water, partially hidden in a grassy clump. Barely the size of a peeper, and about the same size as a cricket frog, this little chorus frog appeared somewhat stockier and its hind legs seemed to be neither so long nor so powerful as those of the southern cricket frog. *Nigrita* is a very dark frog with black markings, and it has a white stripe along its lip.

Among the calls was one which I could not identify. It was vaguely familiar, like a face seen suddenly, and I felt I should know it, but I just couldn't place it. This particular call was being uttered, apparently, by only a few frogs, and since the callers were in a bush quite close at hand it did not take me long to track one down. To my great amazement it was a gray tree frog, *Hyla versicolor,* whose call is one of the better known in the woods of the Northeast. Many frog calls vary greatly from region to region, not because the separate populations are subspecies but simply due to geography, temperature and other conditions.

At first glance, chorus frogs, cricket frogs and spring peepers all look very much alike. However, while they are all members of the family Hylidae they do differ quite a bit from one another. Cricket frogs have slightly warty skins, almost no pads on the ends of their toes, have extensively webbed hind feet, and look like tiny ranids or true frogs.

Chorus frogs have a smoother skin than the cricket frogs, very small disks on their toes, and their hind feet are only slightly webbed.

The spring peeper has the telltale X on its back, extensive webbing on its hind feet and large disks on its toes, as do most members of the genus Hyla. The forward underpart of these toe disks has an irregular surface formed by wedge-shaped cells, and the pad contains a gland that secretes a sticky substance. This enables the tree frog to climb swiftly on apparently unclimbable surfaces, and makes a frog keeper careful to always keep the wire cover closed on Hyla cages.

After some practice one should be able to determine whether a small frog is a cricket frog, chorus frog, spring peeper or a young specimen of another *Hyla* (tree frog) or even a *Rana* (true frog). Identification of the particular species, however, can be extremely difficult and often pre-

Barking tree frog, formerly the largest hylid in the United States.

sents a problem even to a professional herpetologist. Therefore he will usually want to know, when making an identification, where and under what conditions the frog was found. Young frogs, in particular, can be unusually difficult to identify.

To study a body of water such as this pond is not a task that can be accomplished in one evening, or even in several. It could take weeks or months just to catalog the frog life, which abounds with many different kinds, and teems with thousands upon thousands of individuals. Unfortunately I had to cram into a few nights all that I could possibly learn and observe. Despite my best efforts I could only become casually acquainted with this wonderfully rich habitat. I decided that instead of

69

just looking at whatever happened to come along, I would concentrate on finding the particular species that I was especially interested in.

I was fortunate in finding one of these on the first evening. I had been attracted by what seemed to be the call of a tiny insect, perhaps a small tree cricket. It was extremely difficult to separate this weak, high-pitched tinkle from the rest of the multivoiced din of the frog chorus, but finally there it was, sitting on a blade of grass at the edge of the pond, a tiny frog, not more than half an inch in length and very slender. Surprisingly, I managed to catch it and there, almost lost in my hand, was the little grass frog, *Hyla ocularis,* the tiniest of the frogs and toads on the North American continent. It looked almost unreal, and had I not been in search of it and heard its call, I would probably have passed it by as a very young specimen of a somewhat larger species of the hylid family.

I could see the little frog's identification mark, a dark line from the snout through the eye and onto the side of its body. I was holding it loosely in my hand, for fear of crushing it, and it leaped away after only a few seconds. I was fortunate, however, to have had even this brief visit, for the pond was, apparently, on the westernmost edge of the little grass frog's range.

Another frog that I wanted to find, and which I was successful in seeing, though only for a few moments, was the ornate chorus frog, *Pseudacris ornata.* I picked it up in the beam of my flashlight, and even in that unfavorable light I could see that the name "ornate" is truly deserved. It was somewhat larger than the average chorus frog, being more than an inch in length, and was beautifully designed. Color variations are very common in this species, ranging from copper to green. The one I saw was green, with copper-colored blotches on its back, and black blotches on its sides. It had a black mask, not unlike that of a wood frog. What I would have given to have been able to take a color photograph of it! Luck is the nature photographer's best friend—and the absence of it is his worst enemy. Photography at night, particularly in a swamp and using lots of accessories, is anything but easy.

In the South the seasons are not so pronounced as they are in the temperate zone of the North. Cold spells are sporadic and relatively short. Consequently the breeding seasons of the frogs and toads are much longer than they are in the northern states. Some species, such as the cricket frog, *Acris gryllus,* and the chorus frog, *Pseudacris nigrita,* breed, temperatures permitting, throughout most of the winter, and breeding periods of eight or nine months are quite common with many other species.

We were fortunate, during our stay in northern Florida, that there were frequent severe rainstorms which brought out several species of Hyla. Understandably, our obvious pleasure at each shower aroused black looks and loud mutterings on the part of our fellow guests, none of whom were frog watchers.

Near one breeding pool, quite away from the main body of the swamp, I could hear the calls of the squirrel tree frog, *Hyla squirella,* the barking tree frog, *Hyla gratiosa,* and the green tree frog, *Hyla cinerea.* The squirrel tree frog is a small frog, not more than 1½ inches in length, and could easily be mistaken for a small green tree frog, although it is not so slender and lacks the light border stripes. This, however, is only during the frog's "green" phase. It undergoes drastic color changes and frequently turns a dark brown, at which time it closely resembles the Pine Woods tree frog, *Hyla femoralis.* However, there is no mistaking the squirrel tree frog's breeding call. It has an obvious ducklike quality, completely different from the Morse codelike call of the Pine Woods tree frog.

We had seen the green tree frog a few days before, silent in the Wakulla River. Now we heard its call in full chorus. It sounded, to my ears, very similar to that of the Pine Barrens tree frog, *Hyla andersoni,* but faster. The green tree frog can, upon occasion, utter its calls at the rate of 75 per minute. These frogs, calling vehemently and in great numbers, create a formidable chorus which, it is said, sounds like a number of ringing cowbells. This supposed resemblance has earned the frog its vernacular name of "cowbell frog." I must admit, however, that I was never able to detect the similarity. It was not difficult for us to see any number of these fairly large frogs, even though their throat bubble is, in relation to their size, not so large as that of many smaller hylids, whose bubble is sometimes as big as the caller itself. This smaller ratio also holds true for the bubble of the barking tree frog. This tree frog was the largest hylid in the United States until the immigration of the giant or Cuban tree frog, which easily took the championship. The barking tree frog, *Hyla gratiosa*, is more than 2½ inches long. A stocky frog, it is usually green with many dark spots. Its call is quite explosive and said to resemble the barking of a dog, hence barking tree frog.

The pond we were watching appeared to be the almost exclusive domain of these three Hylas, *squirella, cinerea,* and *gratiosa,* with only a few other species calling. One might assume that such closely related frogs, almost all the same size, and breeding in the same pond at the same time, might interbreed, if only by accident. Many studies and observations have been made to determine why this does not happen more frequently. Some theorize that the females are attracted only by the calls of the males of their own species, but considering the intensity of the mating-bent males and their proclivity to seize any suitable object it is surprising to find that the females have much say in the matter. There are several records of hybrids of the squirrel tree frog, *Hyla gratiosa* and the green tree frog, *Hyla cinerea,* just as there are records of hybrids of the American toad, *Bufo americanus* and Fowler's toad, *Bufo fowleri,* but hybridization really occurs infrequently. Whether these hybrids are capable of further reproduction I do not know.

Although I was delighted to see these new frogs there were still two kinds I especially wanted to find, the eastern narrow-mouthed toad, *Gastrophryne carolinensis,* and the oak toad, *Bufo quercicus.* While both of these species have the vernacular name of "toad," they are not related to each other. The oak toad is a true toad, of the family Bufonidae, but the narrow-mouthed toad is not a toad at all. It is a member of the family Microhylidae. Even this name is misleading for, while the frog is indeed "micro" (small), it is certainly not a hylid.

While breeding narrow-mouthed toads make their presence known in no uncertain terms I was unable to locate them or the oak toads by ear. The mating call of the narrow-mouth borders on the grotesque, and reminds me of a group of children imitating the call of a flock of sheep. The call of the oak toad, *Bufo quercicus,* sounds somewhat like the chirping of a young bird. Perhaps it was too early in the year for them to be breeding, but this meant that I would have to find them the hard way, by turning over rocks and logs. This should always be done with maximum caution, particularly in regions where poisonous snakes live. I strongly recommend the use of a rake or similar long-handled tool for the turning. Although I have so far not encountered any rattlesnakes or copperheads, I did turn over a log which harbored a wasp's nest, and the consequences were most painful.

Both the narrow-mouthed toads and the oak toads occupy similar habitats, although the former prefers moist surroundings. I therefore decided to start near the breeding pool which I had previously found so

Eastern narrow-mouthed toad (greatly enlarged).

richly frog-endowed. Several hours of diligent rock- and log-turning finally gained its reward, for under some debris were two narrow-mouthed toads, scurrying away as the light of day struck them.

These creatures are unique in appearance, resembling no other frog or toad except other members of their own family. They are small frogs, or "toads" if you prefer, barely more than an inch long. The name "narrow-mouthed" is extremely well-chosen, for the most obvious physical characteristic of this little creature is its head, narrowing into a snout. Shaped like a pear, with very broad hips and short, wide-spaced legs, it has an awkward and chunky, if not comic, appearance. Nevertheless it is extremely swift and in no time will disappear—running, rather than leaping, with an occasional short hop.

Another unusual characteristic of this frog is a fold of skin across its head behind the eyes, which sometimes, when viewed head on, gives a resemblance to a turtle. The eyes are small and protuberant and look like two popping black beads. The skin is moist, rather smooth, and quite shiny, and its color, as with the majority of frogs and toads, is extremely variable. Usually the basic color is deep brown with darker shadings on the back. None of the toes or fingers are webbed.

All in all the narrow-mouthed toad is hardly a creature that can be misidentified, generically at least. Though solitary in their prenuptial lives, they are massive breeders. However, they manage to conceal themselves so well among plants and debris in or near the breeding waters that they can rarely be seen, although they certainly can be heard. The food of the Microhylids, due to the peculiar shape of their mouth, consists largely of ants and termites, which they pick up in true toad fashion by flicking their sticky tongue at their prey. These are very satisfactory creatures to keep in captivity, for they are not "nervous" frogs and very little disturbs their calm and steady feeding. A close relative of the eastern narrow-mouthed toad is the sheep frog, *Hypopachus cuneus cuneus,* whose call is even more sheeplike than that of

Oak toad (greatly enlarged).

the narrow-mouthed toad.

While the narrow-mouthed toad is strictly nocturnal, the oak toad is active during the day, and since it is quite plentiful in the region I had no great difficulty in finding several. As I held one in my hand I could, again, think of no better description than the one given by Roger Conant in his *Field Guide to Reptiles and Amphibians*—"an elfin toad clad in a tapestry of many colors." Barely an inch long, it is so typically a toad and yet so delicate a creature. The light-colored stripe on its back is one of its field marks, but many other species of toads have the same kind of stripe.

The oak toads I found were pearl gray with a cream-colored stripe and pale orange warts and somewhat resembled immature Fowler's toads in general shape and coloring, although flatter and much more delicate. The best field marks, I believe, are the four and sometimes five dark blotches on its back. While an oak toad can very easily be mistaken for a young toad of any number of other species the fact becomes very evident during the breeding season that it is not immature but is a full-grown adult. Instead of the round balloon-shaped throat bubble of so many other toads the oak toad has a sausage-shaped vocal sac that gives it an almost awkward appearance. These toads are massive breeders and although the individual call seems faint and similar to the chirping of a young bird, a full chorus can be earsplitting.

75

Southern toad. Note the prominent cranial ridges.

I wanted to stay longer in this frog-rich north Florida wilderness of Wakulla, and I also wanted to go farther south to look for certain species which occur only in central and southern Florida. It was a rainy evening when I left Wakulla and I was forced to stop the car almost immediately, for I saw a number of small creatures hopping across the road. They were southern toads, *Bufo terrestris,* very similar to the American toad but much smaller and with prominent cranial knobs. Not far away I could hear their mating call, also similar to that of the American toad, *Bufo americanus,* but somewhat higher pitched and shorter.

I hurried after the toads, just to catch a glimpse of the breeding pond, and was startled to discover several pairs mating in the short wet grass. I had time only to notice that the females were much larger than the males, probably the biggest size difference I had seen in toads, and to worry about what would happen to any eggs laid in the quick-drying grass, then I had to return to my car and get on with the trip farther south.

Before we drove to the Florida Keys we visited a friend in southern Florida and took the opportunity to look for a frog we were particularly eager to find. The greenhouse frog, *Eleutherodactylus ricordi plani-rostris,* is the only frog east of Texas that lays its eggs on land instead of in the water. What is particularly interesting is that the young of this frog develop completely within the egg and have no free tadpole stage at all.

The greenhouse frog came originally from Cuba, but since its introduction into the United States it has become widely distributed in Florida. This tiny frog takes well to human habitat, such as gardens and greenhouses, which has earned the frog its vernacular name; its birdlike, chirping call is delightful and adds greatly to the pleasure of a balmy evening in the subtropical setting.

The female lays her eggs under debris, decaying leaves, and frequently in and under flowerpots. Approximately twenty eggs are laid singly in

The greenhouse frog came originally from Cuba.

Adult greenhouse frog next to egg cluster.

clusters, and look much more like the eggs of certain salamanders than of frogs. Each egg is relatively large for such a tiny frog, and its envelope is thicker than we are accustomed to find surrounding frog eggs. This is probably to afford the embryo better protection against dehydration and the other perils to which land-laid eggs are exposed. After several days two big eyes can be seen through the envelope, and if we touch the egg gently we can induce the embryo to squirm visibly.

Two big eyes can be seen through the envelope of the egg of the greenhouse frog.

The question has frequently been raised as to whether primitive creatures, such as amphibians, are capable of parental care. With some salamanders, such as the marbled salamander, *Ambystoma opacum,* there is strong evidence that the adult frequently guards its eggs, but not much is known about parental care among frogs. Doris M. Cochran, in her book *Living Amphibians of the World,* refers to a relative of the greenhouse frog, the barking frog, *Eleutherodactylus augusti latrans,* which lives in Texas. She says, "The male remains near the eggs until they are hatched . . . wetting them with his urine if the soil around them should become too dry. This is the only known instance of parental care in North American frogs."

78

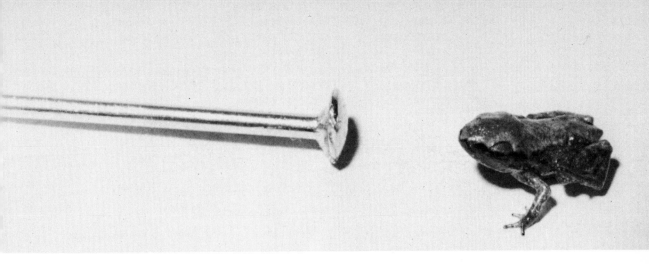

Newly hatched greenhouse frog next to head of common pin, for size comparison.

I have followed the development of several separate egg clusters of greenhouse frogs, however, and when I examined the eggs I very frequently found an adult frog squatting next to the cluster. Although this may be a small point, it makes me inclined not to dismiss the possibility that the greenhouse frog, like its relative the barking frog, offers its eggs certain, if minute, parental care.

Only once was I able to witness the actual hatching of the greenhouse frog's eggs. The tiny froglets emerge from the eggs by means of an egg tooth, similar to the one commonly found on the top of the bill of newly-hatched birds. These minute creatures, which in size and actions resemble tiny fleas, structurally are fully developed frogs, although you may need a magnifying glass to identify them as such. To watch these almost microscopic froglets is a thrilling and awe-inspiring experience. They are so tiny, and so bold. How many of them can possibly make it to maturity? That is the question that must occur to anyone witnessing their birth.

Compared to the mass-laying toads the number of emerging greenhouse frogs is small indeed. And, though it doesn't seem possible, logic says that the chances of a greenhouse frog reaching maturity are greater, proportionately, than are the chances of the American toad, *Bufo americanus.*

One survival problem that faces the eggs of the greenhouse frog continues to puzzle me. Among the many egg clusters I observed, some would be seen, after a few days, to have a few tiny white worms crawling over them. These worms were only a few millimeters in length and thinner than a human hair, but whenever they appeared on the eggs, that cluster died. Within a short time it would be a crawling, slimy mass that soon dried up—like a powder. At first I thought that the worms came from the debris in which the eggs were laid, and in several instances I moved an egg cluster to a terrarium as soon as it was laid. Even there the worms appeared, however, and the eggs died. In a few cases I removed the first arriving worms with a tweezer, and then carefully rinsed the cluster in fresh water. All of these eggs then survived and continued to develop normally. This infestation has remained unexplained, and I can only conclude that at or about the time of fertilization the greenhouse frog eggs must have become infected with the eggs of the worms which had possibly parasitized one of the parent frogs.

The Cuban, or giant, tree frog, *Hyla septentrionalis,* is the largest tree frog in the United States. As the name implies, it is an immigrant from Cuba and the West Indies which has become an established resident in the Florida Keys. Lately it has been mentioned as a source of power failure in Florida and friends sent me several newspaper clippings on the subject. *Current Hi-Lights,* a paper issued for Florida Power and Light employees, said: "Tree frogs have added to FPL maintenance problems . . . croakers hop up poles, straddle two wires on small transformers and cause them to short out. The Operations Department has looked into the problem and learned that the frogs only climb when temperatures range between 55°—75° F. And these climbers are usually the spouseless frogs. 'Squirrel guards' on the poles have proven to be an effective deterrent . . ."

I became very curious to see the frogs that had caused a utility company to add "squirrel guards" and "insulated transformer covers" to their equipment. It was not until we reached Key Largo, however, that a friend was able to introduce me to *Hyla septentrionalis* by plucking two of the frogs from under the eaves of his house, where they spent the day sheltering from the heat of the sun. One of the frogs, was a nearly-five-inch-long female, the other was a male about three inches in length. Aside from their size the most immediately noticeable features were their great glowing eyes and the large adhesive disks on their toes. When we returned to New York I brought these frogs with us so that I could observe them at my leisure. They adjusted well to their life in a large terrarium, and the only problem that developed was in connection with their voracious and almost insatiable appetite. Each frog devoured over a dozen mealworms at their daily feedings, and if I did not withdraw my hand swiftly from the feeding dish I could expect to find one of my fingers attacked and mouthed also. Finally, as an alternate food, I presented the frogs with a supply of crickets that proved highly successful. Not only were the crickets nourishing but they also furnished the necessary daily exercise for the tree frogs, since the crickets, being more adverse to becoming food than the phlegmatic mealworms, forced the frogs to stalk and hunt them if they wished to eat.

I noted that the skin of the Cuban tree frog is moist and rough, and extremely variable in color, changing from a light beige to a deep autumn-leaf brown or olive, and that they are excellent climbers as well as superb jumpers. Occasionally, on warm summer nights when the air was heavy with moisture, the male would utter his call. It was not melodious, but was rather a raucous croaking, somewhat reminiscent of the call of the leopard or pickerel frog, or, as described in Wright's *Handbook of Frogs and Toads*—"This sound is like a jerky pulling of a rope through an unoiled pulley." In the wild the Cuban tree frogs breed in the summer, usually laying their eggs in waters connected with human habitat such as cisterns and flooded basements.

Unfortunately our acquaintanceship had an unhappy ending. While cleaning their terrarium I placed the two frogs temporarily in another tank, occupied by a red eft, the "adolescent" stage of the common newt,

Diemictylus viridescens. One of the Cuban tree frogs immediately swallowed the eft and as promptly regurgitated it. The second frog followed suit, swallowing and again regurgitating the eft. Within a few minutes both Hylas went into convulsions and died. The eft, apparently none the worse for the experience, waddled about as usual. I reported this event to Charles M. Bogert, Chairman of the Department of Herpetology of the American Museum of Natural History. I quote herewith an excerpt from Mr. Bogert's reply:

> The newts . . . are among the few salamanders secreting strong poisons. Naturalists realized many years ago that snakes as well as mammals and birds rarely eat newts, although some species rarely pass up other salamanders. It is of interest to know that the poison of the red eft affords such effective protection against *Hyla septentrionalis.* This large hylid, presumably introduced within relatively recent times to the Florida Keys, may well lack any innate reaction to the red eft, whereas I suspect that frogs native to the areas inhabited by our eastern newt do not prey upon it. . . . I suspect that most predators either learn to avoid animals with poisonous secretions, or have some innate reaction to them, perhaps as the result of selection over thousands if not millions of years. No one has made any extensive investigation of which I am aware, but countless casual observations point to this probability.

It is now late May. In the Northeast, this is the wonderful transition period from spring to summer. The days are warm but not yet hot, the nights are cool but no longer chilly. Many wildflowers and trees are in flower: the entire countryside foams with the massed white of countless dogwood trees. Throughout the woods and meadows the bird calls are at their fullest. Again we return to the pond where, two months ago, we observed the spring peepers and, later, the toads, both of which have long since returned to the woods. The surrounding hills are rosy with wild columbine, and along the paths the once-rare pink lady's-slipper, our best known wild orchid, nods its turbaned head.

In the soggy area around the inlet, the hooded, hidden jack-in-the-pulpit—that favorite plant of childhood, the quaint relation of the skunk cabbage and a common food, when well cooked, of the American Indian—grows tall among its large three-fingered leaves. With almost every step we take along the bank we stir up some living creature. A large tadpole that has been nibbling the grasses at the water's edge scurries back to the safety of deeper water, and green frogs leap into the pond, emitting short, sharp squeals, caused by the quick expulsion of air from their bodies. Although the pond has many residents, permanent as well as transient, it is really the domain of the bullfrog, *Rana catesbeiana,* the largest frog in North America. Most people make their first acquaintance with the bullfrog by ear rather than by sight, for even the casual Sunday hiker hearing the bass "jug-o-rum" emanating from a pond or lake will recognize it as the call of the bullfrog.

Now, as we leisurely walk around our pond we hear this familiar sound, and find the caller quite near the shore in a small inlet, sitting partially submerged and well concealed under a mantle of duckweed. A full-grown bullfrog may attain a length of 8 inches and this appears to be a big one. Dark olive green on top, the snout bright green, undersides white, and the throat slightly yellowish, this is the typical coloring of a bullfrog, although variations do occur. It has a relatively smooth

A large bullfrog floating in the waters of its pond. Bullfrogs are excellent swimmers and divers.

Close-up of bullfrog's head. The large tympanum means that this is a male.

skin, sometimes roughened by small tubercles and it has no ridges or folds
on its back. We stand motionless for a while until the frog, no longer
wary of our presence, accepts us as part of the surroundings and resumes
its call. At close range this call sounds truly formidable but visually it
is a disappointment, for the bullfrog has an internal vocal sac and its
impressive call merely broadens the front part of its body and produces
a flattened pouch under its chin. Since frogs with internal vocal sacs
do not have the darkened, folded throat that enables us to distinguish
between the male and the female of certain hylids or toads with external

vocal sacs, it is fortunate that the bullfrog offers an alternate, visually obvious method of determining its sex. If the frog's tympanum (eardrum) is larger than its eye the creature is a male, if it is the same size as the eye, or smaller, it is a female. This also holds true for several other ranids, or true frogs.

Not far away another frog floats suspended in the water, its legs widespread. This is a favored position among aquatic or semiaquatic frogs, for it enables them to remain on the water's surface and still have mobility to submerge quickly should the necessity arise. The bullfrog is a superb swimmer and diver, due to the great strength of its long hind legs and the large webs between its toes. With a few powerful strokes it can dive to the bottom of the pond at great speed, its entire body streamlined and its eyes shut and pressed downward into its mouth. Since, during this period, the frog cannot see, it usually swims in short, swift spurts, and then stops to reconnoiter.

Due to the development of a nearly transparent fold of skin, called the nictitating membrane, which can be pulled up over its retracted eyes, the bullfrog, and many other species of frogs, is able to open its eyes under water and see where it is going or where danger threatens. On the surface the frog may remain half-submerged with only its snout and the eye ridges, like two observation mounds, showing. In this position it can lie motionless, well concealed from both its prey and its own natural enemies. It is a paradox that both of these classifications can be filled

Nictitating membrane as shown in this close-up of eye of Cuban tree frog.

Water snake sunning itself on a muskrat house. The water snake feeds largely on frogs.

by the same species of animal, for a large bullfrog will eat a small water snake, and a large water snake will eat a small bullfrog.

Although the bullfrog is a voracious eater it rarely hunts its food, but prefers to sit waiting until the food comes to it. Small snakes, crayfishes, mice—indeed anything that moves, including other frogs, as long as it is smaller than the frog itself—are part of its menu. Bullfrogs grab young ducklings in the spring and small birds that come to the pond to bathe, and just as readily snap up a water beetle or insect larva crawling within range on the leaves of the water plants.

The bullfrog is capable of performing enormous leaps, and it can jump several feet to seize an approaching dragonfly, butterfly, or moth. The precision with which the frog accomplishes this is remarkable. I have rarely seen a bullfrog miss its target. However, despite its size, the bullfrog has many enemies. Even a large bullfrog cannot escape the fierce and formidable jaws of the snapping turtle, and mink, otters, raccoons, herons, owls, hawks, and water snakes all relish the taste of bullfrog meat. So does man.

Because the legs of bullfrogs are the principal ones eaten by man,

86

*The bullfrog will eat other frogs
smaller than itself.*

this has had a mixed effect on the bullfrog population. Bullfrog "farm-ing" is not too profitable, considering the cost of labor and other economic factors involved, and therefore most bullfrogs are still hunted in ponds, marshes, and lakes, which has drastically reduced their num-bers in certain areas. However, escapees from sites where they have been penned awaiting slaughter have served to introduce the bullfrog into regions far beyond its natural range. Originally the bullfrog lived only east of the Rockies, but today it can be found almost everywhere in the United States and in many parts of Canada.

As spring turns more and more toward summer the bullfrog's activity increases. Although it calls readily during the day, the chorus is at its peak in late evening. One memorable evening in June I walked toward the edge of a great swamp in Virginia. A mother bobwhite and her six or seven small chicks ran before me in short spurts, tacking from one side to the other of the overgrown dirt road as though they were on wheels. We passed a very elderly, very exhausted red fox, which shied at sight of my convoy and stumbled away as though in fear of the birds. As we arrived at the swamp, a great blue heron flapped slowly over the trees, a figure of dignified departure. And throughout the swamp there resounded the sonorous calls of a hundred or more bullfrogs. The chorus would rise and swell and then die away until it started again with a few solo voices beginning the melody. The droning of the multivoiced bass notes was so loud and so intense that at times it was painful to my ears. The only other sounds were the intense but softer clicking of cricket frogs

87

and the call of a barred owl—all blending together into a wonderful symphony of the night.

In the latitude of New York State the bullfrog rarely breeds before June, when the days and nights have become warm, and the water has reached a temperature of 70°. Bullfrogs are not massive breeders and they do not have to migrate to the water like the spring peepers, wood frogs and toads, for the water is their permanent home. Breeding time is therefore, not an occasion for a mass congregation but simply a matter of the males and females of these permanent water-dwellers finding each other.

A certain amount of local migration does take place, of course, as some bullfrogs leave one body of water to search for another, and hopping bullfrogs are not an uncommon sight on the roads on a warm and humid or rainy late spring evening. The bullfrog eggs are laid in

Even a large bullfrog cannot escape the fierce and formidable jaws of the snapping turtle.

Bullfrog eggs float on the surface of the water like a piece of beaded net.

a mass which, as it floats on the water, forms a film resembling a piece of beaded net. The egg mass contains between 10,000 and 20,000 black-and-white eggs from which the tadpoles will emerge, depending on water temperature and other conditions, within 5 to 20 days.

During the period it takes to metamorphize, a bullfrog tadpole will be olive green in color, with many small black specks, will have an extremely broad tail, and may attain a length of more than six inches, although its size generally will depend in a large degree on the quantity of food it is able to obtain.

A full-grown bullfrog tadpole can be recognized as such simply by its size. From spring until late autumn the tadpoles can be seen lying on the shallow bottom of the pond or on a submerged rock near the shore, but unless we approach very carefully, they will flee to deeper water, or dive into the sand or submerged vegetation. When stalking a tadpole, or any frog, always try to avoid casting a shadow into the pond, for this will immediately spell danger and cause the creature to scurry away.

The bullfrog tadpole has the longest larval period of any frog in the United States and ordinarily, in the North, metamorphosis takes place during July or August of the second or possibly third year. In the Gulf states they will usually metamorphize at the end of their first winter. The process is the same as that of most other frogs and toads. The newly metamorphized bullfrog usually measures about an inch and a half,

89

and greatly resembles some other young ranids.

While a full-grown adult bullfrog, thanks to its size, presents no identification problem, the task is more difficult with the young, which may be mistaken for a green frog, *Rana clamitans melanota,* or vice versa. The simplest, most obvious difference between these two species is the ridge that appears on each side of the green frog's back. Called the dorso-lateral ridge, it is completely absent from the bullfrog.

A full-grown green frog usually measures roughly 3½ inches long, the same size as a young or immature bullfrog three to four years after hatching, or one to two years after metamorphizing. A male green frog of that size is sexually mature, and can emit its banjolike "plunk," which is an additional aid in distinguishing between the two species.

While the sonorous "jug-o-rum" is the call of a mature male bullfrog, young males do, on occasion, feel their oats. I once kept a one-year-old male bullfrog for a few weeks. Every morning at six o'clock, replacing my most dependable alarm clock, it would emit a youthful version of the adult call, the same "jug-o-rum" but almost exactly one octave higher. Two or three years after metamorphizing the bullfrog reaches sexual maturity, and is then ready to start a new life cycle.

Bullfrog tadpole with hindlegs beginning to sprout.

Summer

THE WAY TO THE POND lies through the pleasant woods where the wood frog and the peeper live, and then across an overgrown field, rich in clover, wild roses and the flamboyant butterfly weed, from whose top usually teeters a monarch butterfly. The field is bounded by old apple trees, long since handed over to deer, wasps and flying squirrels, and by the fallen boulders of an old stone fence. If I walk too close to these rocks while the resident woodchuck, which daily grows fatter on the clover, is sunning itself, it will dive into its burrow. Almost immediately, however, it will peer out again and sometimes will give a long, shrill whistle in my direction.

Every step through the grasses sends ahead a burst of grasshoppers and other less strident insects, and frequently the zigzagging long, low leaps of the leopard frog, *Rana pipiens pipiens*. Usually living some distance away from the water, this frog seems to prefer meadows, which obviously accounts for its vernacular name of meadow frog. It is an accomplished jumper, but I manage to catch one and examine it closely.

Woodchuck peering from its burrow.

The leopard frog is a true frog. It is also called the meadow frog.

About three inches long, slender, with long hind legs, it is immediately recognizable as a true frog, a member of the ranid family. Basically brown or green it has irregular dark spots surrounded by light borders on its body, thighs and legs, and very prominent dorso-lateral ridges. Although leopard frogs do not breed in such large congregations as do the peepers or the toads, they collect in sizable numbers in spring, when their snoring mating call can be heard. Now, in summer, they are solitary.

Leopard frogs are probably the most widely distributed species of North American frogs. Their range covers almost the entire United States, except for the Pacific Coast, and far into Canada and Mexico. Owing to this wide distribution the leopard frogs are very well known to many, and pay dearly for their abundance and popularity. They are "harvested" in great quantities, and sold as fish bait and as laboratory animals. In recent years they have been used extensively for pregnancy tests. I am fully aware of the importance and need for using laboratory animals. Many of our medical advances would not have been possible had there not been the opportunity for testing them first on animals. It is, therefore, very hard to take issue with this, provided that the experiments are made under the most humane conditions possible, with the least pain and suffering. We must develop a sense of responsibility in our dealings with creatures under our domain. A larger part in the teaching of biology should be devoted to developing a reverence for life, and the joy and inspiration that can be derived from observing nature's wonders.

Past the meadow the path runs across the brow of a hill, its boulders menacingly covered with poison ivy, and plunges downward toward the pond. Another frog jumps into the sedge away from our feet. It resembles the leopard frog but seems much more orderly, for its spots are square, and are arranged in two parallel rows. It also has orange inner thighs, which the leopard frog does not have. This is the pickerel frog, *Rana palustris*. Although its range is considerably smaller than that of the leopard frog, inhabiting most of the eastern part of the United States from the Maritime Provinces south to the Carolinas and west to southeast Texas, it is extremely abundant wherever it occurs. It rarely ventures far from the water, whether a pond or a shallow stream.

The pickerel frog has very few enemies, owing to a poisonous substance which it secretes from its skin, and that makes it distasteful to many snakes and other predatory creatures. This poison can also be lethal to other frogs that may come in contact with it, so it is best not to keep pickerel frogs in the same container with other frogs.

In the pond the pickerel weed has grown in thick clusters down to the edge of the receding water. On broken and dried stalks hang the crisp thin nymphal husks from which the dragonflies emerged. They are zooming everywhere in the air above the water, snatching insects on the

Pickerel frog.

A dragonfly emerging from its husk.

wing and sailing by in joined tandem as they mate. With their translucent silver or green or double-blue wings they look like creatures from an Oriental water color as they pose gracefully on their threadlike angular legs.

From the pond comes the one sound that is the distillation of all these midsummer days, the "plunk" of the green frog, *Rana clamitans.* This call, resembling the strumming of a banjo, is promptly answered by the "plunk" of a neighboring frog, and, from not too great a distance, another neighbor calls. After this it is again the turn of the first frog. There appears to be almost a rhythm to this monosyllabic "call and answer" game.

What causes these frogs to call? Most of their breeding activities took place earlier in the year, so it can be assumed that these are not mating calls. Many observers believe that these frogs are asserting their territorial rights to the little aquatic area that they occupy. Green frogs stay put. They remain for a great length of time in or near the same spot, waiting for an insect to fly by, or for water insects to swim within gulping distance. If these frogs sat close to one another the competition for food would be severe, therefore each frog apparently stakes out its own territory and "proves" its possession periodically by issuing a determined "plunk."

The green frog, *Rana clamitans melanota,* and its close southern relative the bronze frog, *Rana clamitans clamitans,* inhabit the eastern United States from the Maritime Provinces south to northern Florida. Both the green frog's southern range and the bronze frog's northern range lie in North Carolina, consequently the green frog occupies the larger over-all area.

The name green frog is not a foolproof description, however, for this frog can be brown or olive, or even green. It can be mottled or plain. Its belly is white with dark spots under the legs and the head, and the male's throat is a bright yellow. Attaining a length of more than 3 inches, the green frog can be easily mistaken for a small bullfrog, for the coloring is very nearly the same, but, as mentioned before, of the two, only the green frog has a dorso-lateral ridge, or fold, on either side of its body. And of course the "plunk" belongs exclusively to the green frog.

One week end my wife and I camped near a gentle brook that slowly meanders into the pond. It had long been a favorite spot of ours, and we quickly took inventory to be sure that the green frogs were sitting, as usual, on their submerged stones. Like sentinels they would sit quietly all day, eying various strong-jawed insect larvae and water striders, whose six padded feet ran across the surface film of the water without breaking through. The shadows the striders cast on the bottom of the stream created imaginative patterns resembling eyelet embroidery. The entire setting was relaxing, peaceful, and very quiet.

One night, suddenly, the quiet was broken by a bloodcurdling scream,

Green frog.

like that of a child in distress. Anyone hearing that call for the first time would assume that it had been uttered by some mammal, for surely no lower creature could express such terror. It was, however, the distress call of a green frog.

I was not close to the spot from which the call had come, but in the beam of my flashlight I caught the tail end of what I thought was a large raccoon, as it disappeared into the woods after apparently having feasted on one of the frogs. A frog produces its distress call with the mouth wide open. Often this scream will succeed in startling the predator into relaxing its grip for a moment, and the hapless frog will manage to escape. Even if this maneuver fails, however, the cry will serve to warn the other frogs in the vicinity and give them enough time to take refuge. When I returned to the stream the next morning, all was peaceful and quiet once again. The only clue to what had happened during the night was a fresh set of raccoon tracks in the mud.

Early summer is the beginning of the great exodus from the water. It is the time, in the Northeast, when the transformation from tadpole to froglet or toadlet is completed. Some of them—for example, the toadlets—have spent only a short time as tadpoles, but the young bull-frog has remained a tadpole for at least two years. Just as the mass-breeding adult toads displayed a spectacular courtship behavior, so now the emergence of the newly metamorphized toadlets is also a spectacular mass activity.

A raccoon will feed on frogs. (Michigan Department of Conservation)

Newly metamorphized American toadlet.

We had arranged our visit, we hoped, so as to be at the right time at the right place, and here they were, hundreds upon hundreds of tiny black creatures. The hopping toadlets on the inlet's mud created an illusion that the black mud itself was moving, flowing forward in short jerks. We examined one of the little creatures closely. It is easy to understand why someone who had never seen this exodus before might think that they were minute insects. Pitch black in color, the little toad foreshadows none of the coloring or color patterns so characteristic of the adult. The skin is completely smooth, more like that of a frog than a toad, but there are two faint elevations visible at the back of the neck which, eventually, will develop into the paratoid glands.

The head is large, out of proportion to the rest of the body which appears to be somewhat emaciated. There still is a slight elongation of the body to show where there was once a tail. This is probably the most critical stage in a toad's life. The little toadlets are not only snapped up as food by snakes, turtles, larger frogs, and a host of other creatures but also, because of their thin skin, they often fall victim to dehydration, a deadly enemy of all amphibians.

But there is safety for the species, in numbers. While hundreds, possibly thousands, will be destroyed by one peril or another, others will live and grow. And they grow fast. Very soon the skin will thicken and turn brown. The body will broaden, the paratoid glands and the warts will become apparent, and they will be perfect miniature toads. By then

97

they will have managed to hop to the woods, where we will find them in late summer and autumn.

The toadlets, of course, are not the only Salientia to metamorphize at this time. Not far away, crossing a tiny path that meanders between the thickest rush beds and a low, shaded incline that leads to the woods we find other tiny froglets. They are approximately the same size as the tiny toadlets, but they are beige instead of black and are not so "bloppy." In fact, they are quite well shaped. Closer inspection reveals tiny adhesive pads on the tips of their toes and even a faint X mark on their back. These are the new crop of *Hyla crucifer,* the baby spring peepers.

A full-grown peeper is only about one fourth as long as a full-grown toad, and when it comes to volume and weight the difference between the two creatures is even more striking. It is therefore surprising that their offspring, at the completion of their metamorphosis, are almost identical in size, with the advantage, if any, on the side of the tiny peeper. Probably the reason for this is that the peeper's term of development, from egg to end of transformation, is much longer than the toad's. The toad's eggs hatch fast, sometimes in three days, and I have observed even faster hatching than that. After no more than sixty days their tadpole stage is finished. On the other hand, it takes the tadpole of the much smaller peeper an average of three months to transform. The newly emerged peeper, having had a longer time to develop, thus looks

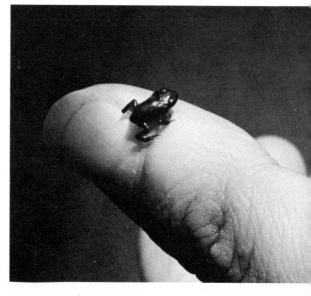

A two-day-old American toadlet. In mass, these can easily be mistaken for minute insects.

Tadpole of green frog with well-developed legs.

very much like the adult in everything except size, while the toadlet looks, to me at least, like a tadpole without a tail, but with thin and tiny legs.

Summer belongs to the young frogs. Sometime during that season the tadpoles of the green frogs, the wood frogs, the pickerel and the leopard frogs, the peepers and the tree frogs, and the bullfrogs all transform. At this early stage in their froghood almost all young ranids prefer to stay close to the water. An exception is the young wood frog, which leaves for its woodland habitat almost immediately after its transformation.

Near the water, frogs are safer from their enemies than they would be on land. Now, as we walk along the shore of the pond, a series of splashes intermixed with short, shrill screams advances before us as little frogs, and big ones, too, dive into the water. This is an instinctive reaction on which frog survival depends. If an enemy—a raccoon, mink, bird, or snake—approaches, a quick dive into the pond is the surest way to safety. Once buried in the mud on the bottom of the pond the frog is relatively safe and the faster it can go from the land to this haven the better its chances for a successful escape. A frog on land, no matter how good a jumper, has very little chance to evade a determined, hungry predator. In addition to being an avenue of escape the water also offers the frog an opportunity to keep its skin moist, another necessity for its survival.

In the shallows of the pond, sometimes clinging to a partially sub-merged stone or twig, we find large green frog and bullfrog tadpoles almost, but not quite, metamorphized. Their shape is fully froglike, but they still have a tadpole's tail. A frog with a tail is a clumsy little creature and would certainly have a difficult time trying to hunt fast-flying insects for food. It is an excellent arrangement, therefore, that it has its own built-in food supply. The little froglet literally feeds on its own tail, gradually absorbing it into its body and, while the tail lasts, requires no other food. As the tail grows smaller the froglet ventures to spend more and more time out of the water, and, when the tail has completely disap-peared, the fully transformed tiny frog is ready to live on land and to hunt small insects for its food.

Summer is also the time of heat waves and often of drought. Most temporary pools have dried up; brooks and streams are reduced to a trickle. The pond has shrunk and much of its formerly submerged bottom now lies bare, crisscrossed with cracks caused by the scorching summer sun. The woods are muggy and buggy. The songbirds call only rarely and the frogs have become silent.

Amphibians are cold-blooded animals, which means that their tem-perature rises and falls in relation to their environment. Equally import-

An almost metamorphized green frog. Its shape is fully froglike but it still has the tadpole tail.

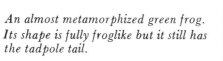

A handsome specimen—the wood frog.

ant to their well-being is the necessity of keeping their skin moist.

During extreme hot spells and periods of drought many amphibians seek shelter, and become quite inactive. At this time the toads frequently dig themselves into the ground in quest of both coolness and moisture. There is, however, much doubt that such behavior represents estivation, or true summer sleep. A lonely peeper may utter a few sporadic calls from the woods to which it has returned and a gray tree frog will occasionally call from the crotch of a tree, usually during a rare and welcome rainy night. Mostly these are silent days, or, as Joseph Wood Krutch calls it, "the dead season." A necessary piece of equipment for a walk through the woods during this time of year is a bottle or stick of insect repellent. It is most important, however, to remember that after the repellent has been applied, you must not touch any amphibian, for its thin skin would suffer severe damage from the contact. I have made it a rule never to apply any repellent to the palm of my right hand, so that I will always have that hand free to pick up a stray frog, toad, or salamander.

A walk through the woods during these hot and humid days can be strenuous but frequently it is rewarding. Most of the wild flowers have stopped blooming, but the ferns are thickly luxuriant under the trees, and near the path the delicate and graceful maidenhair fern forms its wreathlike circles. By a fallen log there is a large cluster of pale and

101

Mink frog. It can be identified by its odor.

ghostly Indian pipes. Their lack of color betrays that they are sapro-phytic plants, feeding on decayed organic matter, and that they lack chlorophyll, the green coloring matter.

Rarely, the green and brown color range is relieved now by a glimpse of the rich deep blue of the bottle gentian. There, blending into the copper-colored floor of the woods, can be found the wood frog, *Rana sylvatica,* to me the handsomest of all ranids. We have met the wood frogs before. They were the earliest breeders in the spring, drab brown at that time to blend with the decaying leaves on the bottom of the pond. Now their postnuptial coloring is beautiful, ranging from light beige or pink to a dark coppery brown. A dark patch running from the frog's eye and covering its tympanum, and a dark line from the eye to the snout,

102

creating the illusion of a mask, make positive identification easy.

The wood frog is slender, approximately 2 to 3 inches long and is an excellent jumper. While most ranids are either aquatic or live reasonably close to water, the wood frog is strictly a land-dweller. It can be found at great distances from the water and is a true creature of the woods. Lycopodia, bunchberries, woodland mushrooms, thick stands of ferns. and all the other rich, redolent, musky plants that live on the moist woodland floor make up the wood frog's habitat, which, except for times of unusual heat and drought, remains cool and damp.

Apparently the wood frog is better equipped to cope with cold weather than any other North American amphibian. Although there is some question as to whether it is a subspecies or just a variant, the northern wood frog, *Rana sylvatica cantabrigensis,* has a range that extends far to the north. The change from the wood frog to the northern wood frog is gradual and is characterized by a shortening of the hind legs, so that the typical wood frog of the Northwest hops much more than does the wood frog of the eastern United States. In any event the frog that lives from Labrador to Alaska and breeds in the shallow pools of the tundra is a very close relative of the wood frog which resumes its breeding activities in the still partly ice-covered pools of our Northeastern woods.

Another frog that ventures far to the north, although not quite so wide ranging as the northern wood frog, is the mink frog, *Rana septentrionalis.* This frog frequents ponds, inlets, and small bays in the mountain streams of the North, and southward through the Adirondack Mountains of upper New York State. In appearance it is somewhat between a leopard frog and a green frog, or even a small bullfrog. Its coloring and pattern are both extremely variable and so is the presence or absence of dorso-lateral ridges.

The one sure identification of the mink frog is not visual but olfactic. When it is handled, its skin may give off an odor reminiscent of a mink, or of stale onions. This odor is produced by a glandular secretion, and is used by the frog as a defense against would-be predators.

I went to the Adirondack Mountains to look for a mink frog late in September, after the close of the vacation season, for I wanted as small an audience as possible as I went from brook to brook smelling frogs. I would catch a frog, rub its skin and smell it. For the first few days I disappointingly had to release all I caught, for none of them could pass the smell test. Eventually, however, in the water-lily-covered inlet of a lake I found a small colony of mink frogs. They were slim, 2- to 2½-inch-long frogs that leaped from lily pad to lily pad when I appeared and smelled ripely when rubbed.

A few weeks later I showed the frog I had brought back with me to a herpetologist friend of mine. He examined the creature, the first mink frog he had ever seen, but when he smelled it he was sure that I had made a mistake. It had absolutely no odor. Later we discovered that a mink frog, in captivity, becomes accustomed to being handled, and no longer makes use of its protective secretion.

The Rocky Mountains are not usually associated in one's mind with frogs or toads. Although as a habitat for these animals this region cannot begin to compare, quantitatively, with the subtropical zone of the Southeast, it nevertheless has a goodly share of residents, some of which can even be found at an altitude of 10,000 and 11,000 feet.

A few years ago I drove through Grand Teton National Park in Wyoming in early June. Over the years I have apparently developed a sixth sense about the presence of frogs and toads, and this, probably, was what caused me to pull the brake on my car near a small pond in one of the marshes that lie in the shadow of the gigantic Teton peaks. As I approached the pond the air was vibrant with that familiar sound which is best imitated by running a fingernail across a comb—the call of the chorus frog.

Summer

While this type of call is common to most species of chorus frogs, each species has its own peculiar pattern and pitch. This one was new to me, and I was most anxious to get a close look at one of the frogs, which were calling in great numbers.

I put my boots on and waded into the pond. As usual, the calling stopped at once and the game of waiting and wading began. Of all the frogs that I have ever stalked these chorus frogs were the most difficult to locate. Finally I had one within ear's range in a small patch of grass and water plants. All was quiet, except for a "slurping" sound coming from the other side of the grassy patch. I had my camera cocked, and was bent over, trying to close in on my quarry when I happened to raise my head, and found myself face to face with a moose, pulling itself toweringly above me. Water was streaming from the pond plants that hung like a Fu Manchu mustache from either side of its mouth. Although I understand that moose are only dangerous during their fall rutting period I was in no mood to test the creature's disposition, and I hightailed it out of the pond as fast as my legs would carry me, my camera and other gear firmly clasped to my chest. This, I am afraid, is the only excuse I have to offer for the absence from this book of a photograph of *Pseudacris triseriata maculata,* the boreal chorus frog.

The boreal chorus frog is considered by many to be a subspecies of the chorus frog, *Pseudacris triseriata,* of which the best known representative is probably the western chorus frog, *Pseudacris triseriata triseriata.* I have always thought that this frog should have been named, more correctly, the "midwestern chorus frog," for its range extends only from western New York State to Kansas and Oklahoma.

Western chorus frog. Its range extends from New York to Kansas and Oklahoma.

As a group, however, the species *Pseudacris triseriata* is very widely distributed, ranging from northwestern Canada to northern Florida, Louisiana and eastern Texas. All are small frogs, barely an inch long, brownish in color, with a white line above the upper lip and, usually, they have three dark stripes on their backs. These stripes however, can be interrupted or broken into spots. The boreal and the western chorus frogs are particularly similar in appearance, but the boreal has shorter hind legs so that it hops instead of leaping.

Actually the differences among all the various subspecies are often very minute, and it takes a great deal of experience to identify these little frogs correctly. To know the location where the frog was found helps greatly, of course. All these creatures are furtive and, even when calling, are very difficult to find. In the North they are one of the earliest amphibians to emerge from hibernation and, like the wood frog, often start their breeding activities while there is still some ice on the waters. The calls of the various subspecies are also very similar, the differences being mainly how fast, and from which end of the comb, you run your fingers.

The West has, of course, its share of toads. One of the most frequently met with is the western toad, *Bufo boreas,* which ranges from Alaska and the Pacific states east into Montana, Wyoming, and Colorado. It lives in a variety of habitats, wherever there is moisture, ranging from an altitude of 10,000 feet down to sea level.

A friend of mine found several of these toads, both males and females, in a trailer camp in British Columbia, where they had apparently made their home near the moist area around the water supply. The western toad is fairly large, attaining a length of five inches, and is subject to great color variations. I have seen several females that were a deep jade green, with prominent warts set in black spots on the back, sides and limbs. *Bufo boreas,* the western toad, is impressive and, particularly with this coloring, truly handsome. All the males that I have seen were

The Western toad, Bufo boreas.

brown, which, however, may have been just a coincidence. Since the male of this toad does not have a vocal sac, its throat is without the usual dark fold of skin and is pale, like that of a female. It does, however, possess a voice, and utters a soft chirping call. Both the males and the females walk slowly, and with dignity, and only hop when danger threatens. It usually digs into the earth, and Robert C. Stebbins, in his *Field Guide to Western Reptiles and Amphibians,* reports that the western toad "seeks shelter in the burrows of gophers, ground squirrels, and other animals."

A very close relative of the western toad, occasionally even inter-breeding with it, is the Yosemite toad, *Bufo canorus.* It is smaller than *boreas,* rarely attaining a length greater than three inches. The Yosemite toad is the toad of the mountains. Its habitat is the mountain meadows and open forests of the High Sierras, where it lives at altitudes of 10,000 feet and higher. It has perhaps the greatest color difference between the sexes of any amphibian in the United States. The female is usually light, with her glands and warts set in large black spots outlined with white, and there are frequently pale splashes of pink or yellow on her sides. The male is usually olive green, with a scattering of small black spots and specks and, like the male western toad, does not have a vocal sac.

The most spectacular toad of the West, however, is the Colorado River toad, *Bufo alvarius;* its six-inch length permits it to vie with, and usually win over, the giant toad for the title of largest North American toad. The Colorado River toad differs from almost all other toads in having smooth skin, but it does have long, oval paratoid glands, several very large warts on its hindlegs, and at least one big cream-colored wart on the jaw, near the shoulder.

Also, in common with the giant toad, *Bufo marinus,* it is extremely toxic. A dog mouthing this toad will shortly become temporarily paralyzed, and a small or weak animal may possibly die. The Colorado River toad, as its name implies, lives along the lower Colorado and Gila Rivers of Arizona, and ranges into Mexico and just across the southeastern border of California. Within this area it can be found almost anywhere there is moisture, and it is reported that its range has spread since it discovered the benefits of irrigation and other man-made wet areas. Many authorities say that this toad can almost always be found beneath cattle troughs in otherwise dry locations.

Later in the year a friend and I were in Los Padres National Forest, not far from Los Angeles. It had been raining for several days, and the little mountain meadow, bordered by coast live oaks and chaparral, was very wet. It was also busy with numbers of very jumpy frogs. Due solely to the agility of my companion we were able to capture a few of these. They were the Pacific tree frog, *Hyla regilla,* probably the most common tree frog of the West. It ranges from southern British Columbia

The most spectacular toad of the West is the Colorado River toad.

Giant toad, Bufo marinus. *Extremely toxic. Note large, pitted paratoid glands.*

south into lower California and east into Nevada and Idaho, and is the only native toad or frog known to be on the coastal islands of California.

Pacific tree frogs are small, from one to two inches long. They are typical tree frogs with well-developed toe pads, although they usually live at ground level and rarely climb anything higher than low bushes. Their hind feet are webbed and they are very active jumpers. The female is usually quite a bit larger than the male. He has a single external vocal sac that inflates into a sizable bubble when he utters his short, rough "krek-krek-krekk."

Particularly noticeable in the Pacific tree frog are its color variations. It has very definite color phases, during which it looks like two entirely different species. During one phase the frog is a deep, even green. At this time it strongly resembles the Pine Barrens tree frog, *Hyla andersoni,* although without that frog's great delicateness. Shortly, however, deeper green markings will appear on its back, and it may then turn a pale buff color with brown markings, during which time the triangle on its head may cause it to be mistaken for a cricket frog.

The Pacific tree frog can run through its entire range of colors, using all variations, within ten minutes, surely a "quick-change" record. At all times, however, it has a black eye stripe that extends down onto its shoulder, although this stripe may not be too visible when the frog is in a dark phase. It breeds from January through July. As noted by R. E. Smith, in Dr. Albert Hazen Wright's *Handbook of Frogs and Toads,* the male discharges a quantity of transparent semen and then slides his feet over the sides and hips of the female. As though signaled by this foot action the female extrudes a clutch of eggs into the cloud of sperm.

A Pacific tree frog in its green phase and, later, in its brown phase.

The Pacific coast is the home also of one of the most unusual salientia in the world, the tailed frog, *Ascaphus truei.* Although this is an inconspicuous creature, it has several notable features. It is, first, the most primitive of all American frogs, and it is the only species that has internal fertilization.

A resident of the Cascade Mountains from British Columbia to northern California, and parts of the Rocky Mountains in Montana and

The tailed frog, Ascaphus truei, *is one of the most unusual American frogs.*

Idaho, the tailed frog lives in the swiftly flowing mountain streams whose temperature remains below 40° all year. A comparatively small frog, only one or two inches long, it is slim, with a flattish body, and varies in color from olive to brown or gray and sometimes even reddish. The female is usually brighter than the male. The skin is granular, at times resembling the greasy plastic from which toys are made, and the male has an unusual number of tubercles on the forearms and feet. The pupils of the eyes are vertical, a feature the tailed frog shares in North America only with the spadefoot toads. A black band or eye stripe can be seen, if

111

the over-all color is not too dark, and the frog's nostrils are unusually far apart.

What makes this frog so truly individual, so impossible to misidentify, is the taillike appendage which the male alone possesses. This, however, is not really a tail at all, not even a rudimentary one. It is an extension of the frog's cloaca, and serves as an intromittent copulatory organ with which the male effects internal fertilization of the female's eggs. This method of breeding is absolutely unique among Salientia, and probably reflects an adaptation to the frog's environment.

Many authorities theorize that in the swiftly flowing mountain streams where the tailed frog lives and breeds, the introduction of the sperm directly into the cloaca of the female is the only way to insure fertilization. The male has no mating call, for it is completely voiceless. It also, obviously, has no vocal sac or sac openings. Here, too, the theory is advanced that the voice has disappeared over the years because it could not be heard above the roar of the rushing waters in which the frog lives.

However, since the tailed frog has no tympanum, or eardrum, either, probably due to the same adaptive reasoning, the female possibly could not hear the male even if he were able to call, although the authorities are not certain whether the creature is completely deaf. So, at breeding time, without a call, the male creeps about on the bottom of the stream until he accidentally meets a female. During the mating period the forearms of the male become greatly enlarged, and he also develops tubercles in the palms of the hands.

Eggs may be laid from May to September. They are relatively large in size, and small in number. Only between 30 to 50 eggs are laid, in strings, which are attached to the underside of submerged rocks. After a month the larvae emerge. They are round tadpoles with large round mouths and are equipped with a triangular adhesive disk on their heads, by means of which they attach themselves to a rock, and are thereby able to withstand the current of the swift-flowing stream. They are also

112

capable of creating suction by the use of their mouth and are thus able to diversify their food by climbing up the face of a rock, and nibbling the algae they find there. Metamorphosis probably does not take place until the following year.

The tailed frog belongs to an old family of Salientia—"old" in the sense that it has many primitive features that are no longer found in most of today's frogs and toads. These include tail-wagging muscles, which, however, have absolutely nothing to do with the male's appendage

Female tailed frog. Note vertical pupil and absence of tympanum, or eardrum.

which gives the frog the incorrect vernacular name of tailed frog. The frogs and toads of the past probably possessed tails, which they have lost in the process of evolution, and the tail-wagging muscles in the tailed frog and its relative, the Leiopelma of New Zealand, are a vestigial reminder of its tailed days. There are other anatomic characteristics, such as the structure of the vertebra, which classify the tailed frog as an old frog. It has a very limited habitat and range. It can live only in the cold, flowing mountain streams of the Northwest. If these waters were to become polluted, as has happened to so many other streams, this small but most singular creature would soon become an extinct species.

Autumn

THE TRANSITION from summer to fall comes almost unnoticed. It is the time of glorious days when the intense heat of the summer sun begins to abate, when the air is dry and refreshing, and the sky is azure blue. The dusty-rose flower heads of the joe-pye-weed stand tall where the meadow meets the woods. The leaves on the trees have begun to turn to red and gold, but they have not yet achieved the splendor they will flaunt a month from now. Goldenrod and wild asters are in full bloom. Staghorn sumac flames against the autumn landscape and even poison ivy displays its leaves in beautiful colors.

In the woods the breeding pools have dried and the bottoms of the depressions are now a mass of dried leaves, stirred by the movements of thousands of tiny spiders. Even a dried pool, however, is useful as a breeding site, for shortly the marbled salamander, *Ambystoma opacum*, will lay its eggs among the leaves on the bottom and will remain with the eggs until a heavy fall rain covers them with water, after which the larvae will hatch.

There is a rustling in the dry leaves throughout the woods. In the underbrush a towhee determinedly scratches for food. These black-hooded, robin-like birds have been with us through most of the spring and all summer but now, with much of the foliage crisp underfoot, its scratching is more noticeable.

There is another rustling in the leaves, quite close by and faint compared with that of the towhee's. Almost at our feet a tiny toad is scrabbling through the leaves. Barely one inch in length, a miniature copy of the American toad, it is obviously one of this year's crop that metamorphized a few months ago. I have, over the years, raised many toads from eggs and I have always been particularly intrigued by their great charm and extreme alertness at this stage of their lives.

A first-year toad has, to a large degree, the same kind of charm that is found in the very young of the higher animals, but it also has an additional appeal of its own which I have found in no other young amphibian: It moves with a grace that contains nothing of the plodding, plopping walk of the adult, and it reacts alertly to every motion around it. Place a

The marbled salamander is another denizen of the frog's and the toad's world.

small insect in the cage with the toadlet and immediately its eyes will flash, trying to seek out the cause of the movement. As soon as it sees the insect it will begin to stalk it stealthily, like a kitten about to pounce. Once within range it will fling its little tongue at the insect with light-ninglike speed. That the insect may be too big for it is no deterrent. At this stage the toad has not yet learned to gauge the size or edibility of a moving object and more often than not will try to snap up a nonedible insect larger than itself.

If the morsel should accidentally prove to be the correct size, it will adhere to the toad's tongue and be flung into its mouth. Other toadlets may have had the same idea and, outdone by their cage mate, they will promptly dart their tongues at it as if to punish the winner. They may even choose to ignore other edible insects in the cage for a moment, in the fashion of a "toad in the manger."

Adult toads behave in similar fashion, but they are much more apt to be realistic in their appraisal of their prey's size and edibility. Everything that moves attracts the young toad's attention. At one time I had an aquarium, inhabited by a few newts, on a window sill. Slightly below them, but almost touching, was a terrarium in which I kept several young toads. In the semidarkness of the unlit room the light from the window would glow through the aquarium, illuminating the newts swimming within it. The toadlets, attracted by movements of the newts regularly sat in a small semicircle, gaping intently at them, and following them with their eyes as the newts swam from one side to another. I could only think of a group of small children concentratedly watching television.

All amphibians shed their skin, but among the salientians the act is probably more apparent when performed by the toads. An adult toad, eating again after a foodless winter, may molt once a month during the spring and early summer, but after that it may shed only three or four more times before winter returns.

Young growing toads shed frequently, sometimes as often as once a week. This molting is associated with growth and is apparently controlled by the thyroid hormone, although the frequency of shedding may also be influenced by temperature, moisture, diet, and other factors that have to do with the well-being of the animal.

Anyone who has observed toads closely can usually recognize the early indications that a molt is about to begin. First the animal begins to "yawn," opening its mouth wide several times, and stretching and twisting its body and humping its back. This exercise apparently loosens the very thin outer skin and separates it from the skin beneath. Now it is as though the toad were inside a thin plastic raincoat, the two front flaps of which are fastened to the corners of its mouth. The toad has to remove the coat in one piece, not in the usual fashion, but by tugging and sucking the coat into its mouth—and then swallowing it.

During this process the toad keeps opening and shutting its mouth and swallowing spasmodically. Occasionally it uses its front feet to rub its body and apparently push the skin along. When it is the turn of the hind legs to be peeled the toad rubs them against the body, and stretches them backward and forward until the skin comes off like a stocking, occasionally inside out. And all the time the two long, black cords of skin keep going into the corners of the mouth, twisting and pulling. At the end just a bit of the cord remains hanging out of its mouth until, with several final convulsive gulps, the toad swallows it all.

If this reads as though it were unpleasant that is how it looks, too, and I believe that the toad would agree, for it appears to be extremely uncomfortable throughout the entire process. Several minutes pass before the toad is itself again, alert, curious and brightly clean in its fresh new skin. The frequency of skin-shedding varies from species to species. The green tree frog, *Hyla cinerea,* is reputed to shed its skin almost every day.

In the woods where we found the first young toad we now find several

118

As a preliminary to molting, the toad first begins to "yawn."

When starting to molt, the Western toad twists its body and humps its back . . .

It keeps opening and shutting its mouth and swallowing spasmodically . . .

All the time the two long, black cords of skin keep going into the corners of its mouth . . .

At the end of the molt just a bit of the skin remains hanging out of its mouth.

more, all within a short distance of one another. When toads have left the water they are no longer gregarious, and these little toads are all bent on taking up the solitary life of an adult. What we are witnessing is the gradual but determined migration of many individual toads, not a group, into the woods.

Autumn

This is also where we again meet adult toads, more than we have seen since their return from the breeding pool. Occasionally we come across one plodding through the leaves on the open rocky hillside which glows with the subdued leathery rust, brown and gold of the oak trees. The toads are more at home, however, farther down the hill in the oak and hemlock woods, where we search for their bright eyes peering from a hole under a rock or from beneath the raised root of a tree.

Usually we know that we have discovered a toad's burrow even before we see the toad, for the earth in front of the opening is clear of debris and cleanly flattened. This is not because the toad is naturally neat but because the movement of its body, as it snatches at passing food, has brushed away the drifted leaves and pressed the earth flat. If the toad notices us it will back further into its hole. Its hind feet are spurred so that they can burrow swiftly backward, even if not so fast or as spectacular as the twisting retreat of the spadefoot toad.

Since this is the beginning of autumn the unlimited food supply of insects, slugs, and worms will shortly run out. Toads, like many other creatures, will soon go into hibernation. Now, in preparation, they gorge themselves.

Fall is the time of the insects, and not only the young toads but the adults too, and all the frogs and tree frogs, take a heavy toll of insect life, which alone should earn them man's gratitude and protection. Insects, of course, are with us from the first warm spring day until the onset of winter, but fall is the time of year when they are most noticeable. A balmy September evening brings out the full buzzing, chirping, stridulating chorus, almost as intense as the spring chorus of the frogs and the toads.

Most prominent of all the insect sounds is the rhythmic rasping of the katydid, best imitated by voicelessly pronouncing its name. Crickets and grasshoppers of all kinds join in, and the chorus is only silenced when the nights become cooler and frost settles on the land. Many mammals are at

121

their most active in the autumn. Squirrels and chipmunks and many other rodents gather nuts and seeds and cache them for the winter. Woodchucks and other hibernating mammals, continue to stuff as much food as possible into their bodies to build the fat that will act as fuel during the time of their winter sleep.

Amphibians, however, slow down as the days and nights grow colder. It always comes as a surprise therefore to hear a call in the woods that we closely associate with spring. The first time I heard it I doubted my ears, but I finally had to accept the fact that a spring peeper was calling in September.

Many frogs and toads develop sex glands in the fall and what I heard was the true mating call of *Hyla crucifer*. This is not unusual. I since have heard peepers call on many pleasant, fairly warm days in every month of the autumn, and have even heard the melodious trill of an American toad late in October. Although I have never observed it personally I have heard reports of egglaying activities in the fall.

Fall, of course, is not the same throughout the country. On the Pacific coast where climatic conditions, even in the same latitudes, differ from those on the East coast, frogs and toads are quite active, even if not necessarily breeding. In the South the southern cricket frog, ornate chorus frog, eastern narrow-mouthed toad, southern toad, and many others continue to breed during the months which are well within what the calendar calls autumn.

Frogs and toads are governed not by the calendar but by favorable climatic conditions. The most important environmental requirements for breeding are water and favorably warm temperatures. Whenever these are met, most frogs and toads will usually breed. Several species of southern frogs and toads breed almost perennially and a great many more do so throughout most of the year, whenever heavy rains occur.

In many parts of the country the difference in seasons does not lie primarily in cold as opposed to hot weather but rather in the presence or absence of rain. The pronounced differences between the four seasons is one of the charms of the Northeast. Fall is one of the longest and most beautiful seasons. It lingers on well into November and is at its height late in October when many deciduous trees display the near-blinding beauty of their colorful foliage.

As autumn progresses, however, amphibian life becomes less and less conspicuous. There still is the occasional call of a spring peeper, and on a warm late-fall day a lone toad may be found in the woods. Even as the days grow colder green frogs may still be seen sitting on the banks of a brook or a pond, diving into the water as we approach, and tadpoles still scurry into the deeper waters. Soon, however, the frogs will bury themselves in the mud on the bottom of the pond, and the toads will dig themselves into the soft earth.

For many years I was told the story of my aunt's potted plants, which were always brought into the house when autumn came. She sat them in a sunny window and one bright morning in February there was a great heaving of the earth in the pot and out came a very sleepy toad awakened by the sun and the regular watering. Tree frogs, too, will seek shelter, probably in a hollow tree. All this preparation is in anticipation of the approach of winter. The periods of frost become longer and longer, and with the advent of the first big snowfall most amphibians will have settled down for the long and all-protecting sleep, the miracle of hibernation.

Winter

THE FIRST SNOW of the season has fallen, and the fields around the pond are white and mysteriously lumpy where the snow has covered and disguised the small bushes and angular broken reeds. Most of the pond is now frozen, although the ice is not yet sufficiently firm to support our weight. Near the inlet where the brook enters the pond the water is still open, and small eddies move slowly beneath the rocks. The pond bottom is visible through the clear water, with its thick layers of dead plant stems and fallen leaves, but no sign at all of any living thing. This is one of the times when we wish we had X-ray vision so that we could see the sleeping creatures beneath the protective layer of pond debris.

The land around us is very quiet. The occasional call of a crow or a blue jay punctuates the silence, otherwise all is still. The woods nearby are white, although somewhat smudged where the small cones of the hemlock trees have dropped and bounced on the frozen snow. Under the shelter of the trees some birds are active. The black-capped chickadee "dee-dee-dees" softly and a small group of them flutter from tree to tree. In the distance the drumming of a woodpecker can be heard. Then, again, all is quiet.

The silence, however, is deceptive. Any experienced observer knows that a great many birds are with us throughout the winter, not only in or near the sea but also here in the fields and the woods. And birds are not the only creatures to remain active. There are others about, so furtive in their habits that only a seasoned naturalist endowed with stamina, patience, experience and luck can find them. But even an observant novice can soon detect the betraying signs left by winter residents. In and near the woods squirrel tracks are common and easily identified. They usually lead directly to a tree, and betray any secret hideout that the squirrel may have had. Also, telltale mounds of nut shells divulge where the squirrel paused for a snack.

Often we find reminders of another kind of meal, a tiny drop of blood staining the snow. What little creature has fallen victim to what hungry predator? A deer mouse perhaps? There are plenty of them about. We find their delicate footprints on little mounds of snow in the thicket where, in a small underground burrow, they find shelter and the food they stored away earlier in the year. When they do venture out many of them become the main staple in the diet of predators, which, by their very nature, cannot hoard food for the winter but require a constant supply of fresh protein in order to survive. Life is harsh for the creatures that remain active during the winter and their tracks can tell us much about their habits. Tracking is relatively easy, and can be an absorbing and mentally and physically stimulating pursuit for anyone interested in the study of wildlife.

During the winter the red fox depends for food on the creatures that do not hibernate. (Michigan Department of Conservation)

The World of the Frog and the Toad

Winter's cold and storms are a great burden to many animals, but an equal peril is the absence of their food supply. Many birds and some mammals follow their food by migrating to favorable climates. Others endure the hardships of winter and, in the process, may succumb to starvation or exhaustion. Winter is arduous for the white-tailed deer, which depends on browsing, and many nonmigrating birds find the seed supply scarce. Squirrels, deer mice and other rodents take autumn's plentiful supply of seeds and nuts and cache them in safe underground spots they may be able to find again.

But some creatures have been biologically endowed with one of nature's more effective methods for coping with the absence of a food supply. They are able to slow down to a state of complete inactivity in that form of suspended animation called hibernation. These creatures too have stored food away, not in underground caches but in the form of their own body fat. Most of the hibernating mammals apparently fast before going into winter quarters so that their alimentary tract will become empty; then, by greatly reducing their fat-consuming activities, they are able to survive for long periods with no food intake whatsoever. During this deathlike sleep, their heartbeat and respiration drop to a small fraction of the normal rate and are, in fact, barely detectable. Body temperature drops close to freezing, and blood circulation becomes very sluggish. Woodchucks, jumping mice, and certain bats are only a few of the mammals which thus survive the winter. Questions that still remain unanswered include: Why do some bats hibernate while others migrate? Why do jumping mice and woodchucks hibernate, whereas deer mice and squirrels do not?

Mammals, however, are not the only creatures that hibernate. Among the many others that cope with winter in this fashion are insects, snails, and reptiles and amphibians, both tailed and tailless. Amphibians are "cold-blooded" animals and, as the temperature around them drops, so does the temperature of their bodies. The amphibian becomes torpid and

Hibernating toad.

seeks shelter where it can survive without freezing to death. While the drop in temperature appears to trigger the prehibernation behavior of the amphibian, other conditions also would seem to be factors. One of these, possibly, is the lessening amount of daylight during the shorter autumn days.

Not all frogs and toads hibernate in the same fashion. Toads dig into the soft earth, sometimes three feet down. Others seek shelter in protected hollow logs and trees, or crawl under piles of fallen leaves and other debris, all of which offer good insulation as well as moisture. Some frogs go to the bottom of the ponds where, under the matted leaves and mud, they spend the winter. Frogs are air-breathing creatures and at temperatures above 40° they must come to the surface for air. However, when the temperature falls below 40°, they can obtain oxygen from the water through their skin, and thus are able to survive long periods on the bottom of the pond, with no danger of drowning. For some unexplained reason, many hibernating frogs congregate in large numbers and can be found, packed together, on the bottom of a popular pond. Could a possible shortage of suitable hibernating sites account for this?

An amphibian dug up from its hibernation site looks very much as though it were dead. It can be turned over on its back, a position no healthy frog or toad would permit for an instant if it were awake, and will remain there, with no apparent movement in its throat to indicate that it is breathing.

Hibernation, in itself, is no guarantee of survival. Winter takes a heavy toll of hibernating wildlife, and the thin-skinned, cold-blooded amphibians are much more likely to succumb to the cold than are warm-blooded furry creatures. If the temperature of a hibernating animal falls below freezing it will surely die. There are many reported observations of frogs having survived, although frozen within the ice. Whether these reports are correct I have never been able to ascertain, but since snow and ice have some insulating qualities, it is impossible to completely discount such reports.

During a severe winter a pond may freeze all the way to the bottom, including the protective layer of mud and debris. Then the frogs hibernating there will probably die. Fortunately, during most winters there is a layer of water left between the ice and the bottom of the pond, allowing the amphibians and other denizens of the pond to live through the winter. In their quest for suitable hibernation sites many amphibians display poor judgment, and frozen, dead animals are frequently found in crevices of trees, logs, and other unprotected locations. The toads, whose safety is in the earth into which they dig, must be sure to burrow deep enough to escape the freezing of the topsoil. No amphibian can survive in regions where the ground is permanently frozen. The northernmost range of our most northern amphibian, the northern wood frog, ends where the permafrost begins.

Tadpoles, like most fishes, do not hibernate, but spend the winter in the deeper part of the pond, where the ice does not usually reach. The tadpole stage is a growing period for the frogs and they must eat to grow.

Winter

These green frog and bullfrog tadpoles live on algae and other plant matter and even in winter there is no dearth of such material on the bottom of the pond. For better protection, as the winter grows colder, the tadpoles may bury themselves under the debris. Seining the pond bottom almost always nets a few tadpoles, mixed in the viscous mud with dragonfly nymphs and various tiny, wiggly insects.

But from where we stand on the shore of the pond no life is visible. The crows have ceased their cawing, and gray icy silence surrounds us. There is nothing as silent as a freezing winter day. A cold wind causes us to turn up our collars, and we walk away, leaving only our tracks behind. Our thoughts are with those animals under our feet that, throughout the land and the water, are snugly and peacefully sleeping out the winter. Almost subconsciously we count the weeks ahead. First will come the spotted salamanders . . . then the wood frogs . . . then the peepers . . . then the toads. . . . How many more weeks?

Photographing
Frogs and Toads

WILDLIFE PHOTOGRAPHY is a highly specialized field and cannot be learned in the proverbial six easy lessons. It requires years of experience, with their accompanying trials and errors. Patience and, often, physical stamina and endurance are indispensable. A good basic working knowledge of photography is an absolute prerequisite, and so is a field knowledge of natural history, which will, in turn, be substantially enriched by doing wildlife photography. The rest is up to the creativity and imagination of the photographer and, to be frank, to good luck. Although practice is the best teacher, much can be learned from the books written on this subject, and for the names of a few of these I refer the reader to the bibliography at the end of this book.

I would like to offer a few suggestions to the reader which may prevent some failures, disappointments and unnecessary expenses.

Usually I use a Hasselblad 500 C. This is a $2\frac{1}{4}$ x $2\frac{1}{4}$ camera, and for many reasons I prefer this size to a 35-millimeter camera. As I do most of my black-and-white printing myself, I prefer to work from a larger negative, which is less subject to annoying scratches and dust spots. For color photography also I find the larger transparencies more satisfactory, as do many publishers, although in recent years 35-millimeter transparencies have become quite acceptable for reproduction.

The Hasselblad is a single lens reflex camera and so, of course, are a great many of the better 35-millimeter cameras. This type of camera lets the photographer see exactly what will appear in the picture, without having to worry about the parallax problems which arise when twin lens reflex cameras are used at close range.

Interchangeable lenses are almost a must in wildlife photography, and the Hasselblad is ideally equipped in this respect. So, of course, are many other good cameras in the 2¼ x 2¼ and 35-millimeter sizes. For close-ups I use extension tubes as well as, on occasion, front lenses. This enables me to get close enough to a small subject to obtain an image sufficiently large to fill the frame. For longer distances I use a 250-millimeter telephoto lens, which would be insufficient for bird or mammal photography but is, in my opinion, perfectly suited for photographing amphibians, particularly if used in connection with extension tubes and/or front lenses. In this manner I can remain from one to seven feet from the subject, and still obtain a frame-filling image.

One further advantage of this camera, shared with at least one other make, is its interchangeable back. Thus I can have one back loaded with black-and-white film (usually Kodak Plus-X Pan) and another back loaded with color film (Kodak EX 120).

A good sturdy tripod is indispensable, particularly when shooting with a telephoto lens, although, under certain conditions, hand shots are inevitable. A good gunstock is helpful with the latter.

I use Acufine developer for processing the Plus-X Pan film. This developer raises the ASA rating of the film to 320, and gives a very good, almost grainless negative. There are, of course, other developers which increase the film speed satisfactorily, and my use of Acufine is simply a matter of personal preference.

Aside from natural light the only other source of light that I can recommend is an electronic flash which can be used on both AC current and on batteries. The latter will enable you to take the flash unit into the field. Regular flash entails changing the bulb after each shot, which, in the field, can be annoying. Also, you will be dealing with shy creatures, and any unnecessary movement, such as groping for flash bulbs, may turn your subject even more noncooperative than usual. Electronic flash units come in all sizes and price ranges. I use a moderately priced Heiland unit which, as far as my work is concerned, fills the bill perfectly. To avoid harsh shadows, particularly with smaller subjects, I use a ring light adapted to the electronic flash. If at all possible I use the ring light in combination with another light, for additional side or back lighting. This gives the picture a three-dimensional quality.

Whenever practical, I photograph outdoors, in the animal's natural habitat. Certain pictures can be obtained no other way. To venture into a swamp at night, heavily draped with equipment, is not a simple feat. I suggest that before embarking on such an undertaking for the first time a dry run should be made during the day, when visibility is good. As we observed with spring peepers and other frogs and toads calling from the water, patience and experience is needed to locate them. This is difficult enough without carrying photographic equipment.

To find a caller at night requires a flashlight of course. A partner can be most helpful, as two flashlights offer the possibility of finding your subject by triangulation. The night photographer should wear a head-lamp, which will free his hands. Once the subject has been located, the shooting can begin. And here even an experienced photographer can be up against a serious pitfall. In his excitement he may not notice the stray blade of grass, or similar matter, which may blow into the picture, and spoil it. This has happened to me many times, and I pass this along as a warning.

Photographing small animals under controlled conditions—that is, indoors—is, morally, perfectly all right, so long as the photographer does not state that the picture was taken in nature. I have photographed many frogs and toads in this manner, particularly the smaller ones. The problems of lighting, and other outdoor problems, are thus greatly diminished, and allow the photographer to concentrate on the subject.

Great care should be taken, however, to make sure that the setup is similar to the subject's natural habitat. I prefer to keep the setup as simple as possible, and to concentrate on taking a good photograph of the subject itself.

Even when photographing under controlled conditions I prefer electronic flash to any other light source. Some photographers use floodlights, which have the advantage of allowing you to supervise, in advance, how the subject will be lit. These lights throw off so much heat, however, that they can seriously dehydrate or even kill the frog or toad. Even when taking photographs with electronic flash I frequently sprinkle my sitters with cold water to keep them comfortable.

Not all frogs and toads are willing models. As a matter of fact, practically none of them are. I once took a photo of a large Cuban, or giant, tree frog, *Hyla septentrionalis*. It poised for a jump, and in that position I was able to get an excellent photograph. The moment the shutter clicked, the frog jumped directly onto the lens of the camera. Toads, too, are most obstinate in their determined efforts to hop out of camera range. Some photographers suggest placing difficult subjects in the refrigerator first to slow them down. This usually takes away the frog's alert and lifelike expression, and makes it look sluggish and, sometimes, even stuffed.

If I were asked what I consider to be the most important requirement for frog and toad photography, particularly under controlled conditions, I would say that it is patience and understanding for the animal. Do not expose it to any unnecessary suffering or discomfort, even if it means losing a shot. There will be another.

Cuban tree frog poised for a jump.

Keeping Frogs and Toads in Captivity

KEEPING FROGS AND TOADS in captivity is not only an interesting and stimulating avocation, it is also indispensable for serious study of these animals. To observe one specific individual in the wild, for an extended period of time, is usually highly impractical. Longevity studies of frogs and toads, for example, certainly can best be made with captives. In the wild, an aging animal has very little chance of survival. It encounters ever-increasing difficulty in hunting for food and, because of its decreasing alertness, is almost certain to fall prey to a predator.

At one time I caught a large female gray tree frog, *Hyla versicolor*, that was obviously an old one. However, she thrived in captivity, became quite tame, and readily accepted food from my fingers. I had kept her for more than five years when she became very slow and sluggish, and had every appearance of being senile. She could no longer climb, and unless propped in the crotch of her favorite branch she would slowly topple. Her tongue lost its elasticity, and when she tried to snap up her food she was unable to reach even the nearest morsel and had to have the food brought to her mouth. Nevertheless, with patient care, she survived another spring and summer, and in the autumn she simply slept away. I don't know what her age was, but it certainly was greater than could possibly have been reached in the wild. Other studies too, such as feeding habits, can best be made with captive individuals. I wonder, for instance, whether many have ever seen a spadefoot toad feed except in captivity.

Not all frogs and toads lend themselves equally well to being kept in confinement. My experience with ranids has not been too good. These large frogs are both excellent jumpers and swimmers, and a terrarium does not seem to offer sufficient room for exercising these faculties. This may be only a personal experience, however, for I have seen a large bullfrog kept for several years in a small display cage, barely larger than the frog itself, and the frog seemed to thrive. I have been more successful in keeping bufos and hylids, although even among these species I have had some individuals that just weren't "happy," and I thought it best to release them. If an animal is to be released it should never be placed in a strange habitat where it probably would not survive. It should be released as soon as possible, and in a habitat similar to the one where it was found. An animal kept in captivity for any length of time may not be able to readapt to the wild, and if it has refused to eat it may have become so debilitated that it will no longer be able to cope with the rigors of the outdoors.

There are several important factors which must be considered for successful frog-keeping. The first is proper housing. The best container I have found is an ordinary rectangular aquarium or terrarium, constructed with a metal frame, slate bottom and glass sides. A tank approximately two feet by one foot by one foot is suitable for larger frogs or toads, and one about sixteen inches by ten inches wide and high will suffice for smaller ones.

At one time I was lucky to find in a junk shop an old popcorn dispenser, two feet high and fourteen inches long and wide, with glass sides. This made perfect housing for the larger tree frogs, for it gave them ample room to climb on the branches I placed inside. I have found that very small, newly metamorphized tree frogs are best kept in a wide-mouthed gallon jar. The jar should be covered with a fine net or a nylon stocking, and the jar cover placed on top. The cover should have five or six holes punched in it, and the prongs surrounding the holes should face outward, so as not to injure the frogs if they climb near the top. The net serves to hold any small insects that may be introduced for food. The bottom of the jar should be covered with moist moss or, in a short emergency, with wet, crumpled paper towels. A stick may be included for climbing, but the tiny tree frogs usually seem satisfied with the glass.

There are three main types of habitats used for keeping frogs and toads: the woodland terrarium, for toads, woodfrogs and other non-aquatic salientians; the semiaquatic terrarium, for frogs which usually live in water; and a regular aquarium for tadpoles.

The first step in preparing all three of these different habitats is to put at least one inch of washed aquarium gravel on the bottom of the tank. This serves to contain impurities in the aquatic habitat, and to hold excess water in the dry terrariums. For a woodland terrarium, spread at least two inches of earth evenly on top of the gravel. Good rich loam from the woods is preferable to the "purified" earth that is bought in bags in city stores. The other must is a glass or china dish to hold water in which the animal can soak. The cage may look better if the dish is sunk into the earth unobtrusively, but the constant splashing of the water may soon make the earth too wet.

Also include a small feeding dish into which the worms and insects should be put. If these are placed directly on the earth they may immediately dig under, or in other ways become more difficult to be picked up. All frog and toad cages should be covered with a piece of glass. This not only prevents the animal from escaping but it also helps to retain the moisture.

The tank may contain some plants that can be found in the salientian's native habitat, such as moss, ferns, and other attractive objects. You may shortly find, however, that the plants do not last. Salientians, toads particularly, will dig, and they will usually uproot your decorations. I have found that the best items to place in a toad's cage are a few dried leaves to scuffle in, some inverted pieces of bark, under which the animal can hide, and, if there is room, a small log to sit on. For smaller salientians, other than toads, you can include one small plant in a flowerpot. This will keep the plant from being uprooted, and many frogs and toads like to climb on the pot. I have kept a few narrow-mouthed toads for several years. At first I placed in their tank just a few pieces of bark and some moist moss, under which they burrowed. Shortly thereafter I added a potted plant. To my surprise, one of the toads spends even the daylight hours climbing about on the leaves of the plant. The remaining toads still burrow during the day, but at night they too climb up the sides of the pot and sit on the plant.

Aquatic or semiaquatic frogs should be kept in a terrarium that is partly land and partly water. This can be constructed by building one end of the terrarium above water level with gravel or small, well-balanced stones, or pieces of wood—or, alternatively, by sinking a large water container into the earth at one end of the tank. I have kept bullfrogs and green frogs in large water-filled tanks which had a few big stones set in the middle. The frogs could then swim energetically or climb on the rocks and just sit.

Care should be taken not to include salientians of greatly different sizes in one tank, as the larger frogs may attempt to eat the smaller ones. Be careful not to include pickerel frogs, *Rana palustris,* with other salientians, for their skin may prove toxic to other frogs coming into contact with it.

Tadpoles, of course, must be kept in a true aquarium. Tap water should never be used to fill the tank unless it has been properly aged by letting it stand in an open container for at least two days or has been otherwise dechlorinated. The tank should contain some algae, a few water plants or duckweed on which the tadpoles can nibble, and possibly a few pond snails to scavenge and do the tank cleaning. As soon as the tadpoles begin to metamorphize, one end of the tank should be built up from a gentle slope or a stone or other solid object should be put into the tank, so that the emerging froglets or toadlets can climb out and not drown.

No terrarium or aquarium should be placed in direct sunlight for any length of time. During hot summer days particularly, the glass enclosure can become extremely hot, and the cold-blooded inhabitants, with no internal temperature control, will probably die. Also, under no condition should a terrarium ever be allowed to dry out. Most frogs and toads can live a great length of time, sometimes months, without food, but will die within a few days if there is no moisture available.

Keeping frogs and toads during winter is a different matter. I usually keep terraria, containing frogs and toads that normally hibernate, in a cool place. These terraria contain earth, dried leaves and debris into which the animals can burrow. These tanks, also, are lightly sprinkled with water from time to time, so that the animals will not dehydrate. I have found this system very satisfactory and have rarely lost a hibernating animal. Frogs and toads from warmer parts of the country are kept in a heated room, and their normal activities will usually continue uninterrupted.

For transporting frogs and toads it is best to use a glass jar with a screw top. The lid should have five or six holes punched in it, prongs out. In the jar place wet moss, leaves or paper toweling. If you have no bottle or similar object on hand, and unexpectedly find a frog or toad you want to carry home, line your handkerchief with wet leaves and tie it loosely but securely, thus forming a small sack.

Feeding frogs and toads can be one of the most difficult problems. If you live in the country natural food is relatively easy to get, otherwise you will probably have to resort to commercial substitutes. Although earthworms are the ideal diet for the larger frogs and toads they are difficult to obtain in cities. Fishermen buy them, prepackaged, in stores, but apparently fishes are not so discriminating as toads or frogs, for I have never been able to induce one of these to swallow a packaged worm. They will snap at the worm as it moves, just as they will snap at anything that moves, but as soon as they taste the worm they spit it out violently and keep rubbing their mouths afterwards, as though to remove the taste. Probably whatever it is the worms are packaged in gives them an obnoxious taste.

Larger frogs and toads can usually be fed mealworms, which are obtainable from pet shops or mail-order houses. Caution in feeding is, however, advised. The chitin, or outer coat, of mealworms can be harmful, particularly to smaller individuals. I once saw a mealworm virtually eat its way through a young green tree frog, *Hyla cinerea*. When feeding these worms to smaller or more delicate frogs I usually wait until the worm sheds its skin, and then it is a truly relished morsel.

Small clumps of raw hamburger, prepared with beef from which all the fat has been removed, and which is scraped with a knife instead of ground, are also readily accepted, especially by young toads. The meat has to be wiggled with the end of a straw to simulate live prey, for frogs and toads will not eat anything that does not move.

Toadlets eagerly eat food presented on the end of a toothpick.

A most satisfactory food for tadpoles and all small salientians is tubifex. These small aquatic worms can be purchased in most pet shops. It is easy to keep them alive in a small jar with a perforated lid if they are washed daily in cold water, and kept in the refrigerator. Although these worms are primarily used as food for fishes and other aquatic creatures it is not difficult to feed them to small terrestrial frogs and toads. Lightly dry a small batch of the worms on a paper towel. Then, with the end of a straw, dangle the worms in front of the small frog or toad. Results can almost be guaranteed. Newly metamorphized toadlets or froglets will tackle a halfworm at a time, and small but adult salientians, like the narrow-mouthed toads, will gobble several batches during a feeding. Small toadlets are raised on tubifex until they are big enough to take larger food. They then graduate to scraped beef or soft mealworms, also offered on a stick and, later, to soft mealworms in a dish. By the time they manage to snap their tongues skillfully at moving worms they are ready to tackle regular mealworms and, as adults, earthworms. Large bullfrogs and other large ranids are best fed earthworms or mealworms dangled from forceps or tweezers to simulate flying insects.

One point cannot be repeated too often. Do not overcrowd your terrarium. Outside of the breeding season practically all frogs and toads are solitary creatures, and they need "territory."

Cleanliness is one of the most important prerequisites for successfully keeping captive frogs and toads. They are very susceptible to certain diseases, particularly to one called "red leg." If this disease appears, place the sick animal immediately in a .15 per cent solution of common salt and water. This may cure it.

Your interest in these creatures will be stimulated if you keep a small notebook by your terrarium, and carefully enter the details of the daily life of the frog or toad. Some small thing that you have noticed and noted down might prove to be a previously unknown fact about the animal.

Keeping Frogs and Toads in Captivity

Frogs and toads are creatures of the wild. While many of them will do well in captivity, it should always be kept in mind that they do not really belong there. Keep a few of them if you must. Enjoy them and give them the best care possible. If you are not prepared or able to do so, leave them where they are. Wild animals are not toys. You may have noticed that throughout this chapter I have never referred to them as pets, for that they are not, nor are they meant to be. While they may, with good care, become tame enough to take food from your fingers, they cannot become members of the household as do dogs or cats. They should not be handled any more than is absolutely necessary for their own well-being, and if they must be handled, it should be done as carefully and as gently as possible.

Pick up a large frog or toad by gripping it gently behind its forelegs. Never hold a frog by its hind legs. This could seriously injure the creature, particularly if it tries to escape from your grasp. Most of us, when we come upon a rare species or a species that is new to us, are tempted to overcatch. We must control this impulse lest we deplete an already rare or endangered species. In any event, never catch more individuals than you can accommodate and care for properly. Though keeping a frog or toad in captivity can be a source of enjoyment by observing them and listening to their calls, it cannot compare to the pleasure to be derived from being outdoors on a warm evening and listening to their calls as part of the wildness in which, Thoreau said, "lies the preservation of the world."

Species and Subspecies

HERE ARE THE COMMON AND SCIENTIFIC names and ranges of the frogs and toads which are referred to in this book. These names follow those of Roger Conant in *A Field Guide to Reptiles and Amphibians of the United States and Canada East of the 100th Meridian* and Robert C. Stebbins in *A Field Guide to Western Reptiles and Amphibians*.

TRUE FROGS
(Family Ranidae)

Bronze frog, *Rana clamitans clamitans*—southern North Carolina to north-central Florida and west to eastern Texas. Inhabits the Mississippi Valley north to approximately the mouth of the Ohio River.

Bullfrog, *Rana catesbeiana*—Atlantic Coast from Nova Scotia to central Florida, west to Wisconsin, Nebraska, eastern Colorado and eastern New Mexico. Has been introduced into many areas west of the Rockies and in the Hawaiian Islands, as well as Mexico, Cuba, Japan and Italy.

Carpenter frog, *Rana virgatipes*—inhabits only the Coastal Plain from south-central New Jersey to eastern Georgia.

Green frog, *Rana clamitans melanota*—Maritime Provinces south to North Carolina and west to Minnesota and eastern Oklahoma. Has been introduced into Newfoundland.

Leopard frog, *Rana pipiens*—the leopard frogs have the widest range of any amphibian in the United States. From southern Labrador south to northern Georgia, west to the Pacific states, and have been introduced into some isolated areas in California. Ranges north, in Canada, to Great Slave Lake.

142

Species and Subspecies

Mink frog, *Rana septentrionalis*—Labrador and Maritime Provinces west to Minnesota and southeastern Manitoba, and south to northern New York.

Pickerel frog, *Rana palustris*—Maritime Provinces south to the Carolinas, west to Wisconsin and southeastern Texas.

Wood frog, *Rana sylvatica*—along with the northern wood frog, this frog has the northernmost range of any North American amphibian. Labrador to Alaska, south in the East to the southern Appalachians. There are isolated colonies in Kansas, Colorado, Wyoming and Idaho.

TRUE TOADS
(Family Bufonidae)

American toad, *Bufo americanus*—in northeastern United States and Canadian Maritime Provinces west to southeastern Manitoba; south through Minnesota and Iowa to Missouri and northeastern Kansas; east to Virginia and south to parts of North Carolina, western South Carolina, northern Georgia, and northern Alabama to Mississippi.

Colorado River toad, *Bufo alvarius*—lives only around the lower Colorado and Gila Rivers of Arizona and southwestern New Mexico. South to northwestern Sinaloa, and in extreme southeastern California.

Fowler's toad, *Bufo woodhousei fowleri*—central New England south to the Gulf Coast, except for most of the southern Coastal Plain and Florida. West to Michigan, northeastern Oklahoma and eastern Louisiana.

Giant toad, *Bufo marinus*—in the United States lives only in extreme southern Texas, and has been introduced at Miami, Florida. It ranges, however, as far south as Patagonia.

Oak toad, *Bufo quercicus*—Coastal Plain from North Carolina to eastern Louisiana, and south through Florida and the lower Keys.

Southern toad, *Bufo terrestris*—Coastal Plain from southeastern Virginia to the Mississippi River and south through Florida and the lower Keys.

143

Western toad, *Bufo boreas*—Pacific Coast as far east as the Rocky Mountains, and from southern Alaska south to northern Baja California.

Yosemite toad, *Bufo canorus*—lives only in the High Sierras of California, from Alphine County to Fresno County, on mountains over 6,000 feet.

TREE FROGS
(Family Hylidae)

Barking tree frog, *Hyla gratiosa*—Coastal Plain from North Carolina to southern Florida and eastern Louisiana. There are a few isolated records in Alabama and Georgia, and it has been introduced in southern New Jersey.

Cuban tree frog, *Hyla septentrionalis*—In the United States lives only in extreme southeastern Florida and the Keys.

Gray tree frog, *Hyla versicolor*—New Brunswick (Canada) south to western Florida and west to eastern North Dakota and central Texas.

Green tree frog, *Hyla cinerea*—Delaware, Maryland, and Virginia Peninsula south to Florida Keys, west in the Gulf Coast Plain to central and southern Texas and north to southern Illinois.

Little grass frog, *Hyla ocularis*—Southeastern Virginia south to the southern tip of Florida and west to southeastern Alabama.

Northern green tree frog, *Hyla cinerea evittata*—upper tidewater Potomac and parts of the Delaware, Maryland, and Virginia Peninsula, and the Coastal Plain in Maryland and Virginia, where its range blends with that of the Green tree frog.

Pacific tree frog, *Hyla regilla*—southern British Columbia south to Baja California and east to western Montana and eastern Nevada. On the islands off the coast of southern California.

Pine Barrens tree frog, *Hyla andersoni*—lives only in south-central New Jersey, except for a few scattered groups in North Carolina and Georgia.

Pine woods tree frog, *Hyla femoralis*—Coastal Plain from Maryland to southern Florida and eastern Louisiana.

144

Southern spring peeper, *Hyla crucifer bartramiana*—lives only in southern Georgia and northern Florida.

Spring peeper, *Hyla crucifer*—Maritime Provinces south to northern Florida and west to eastern Texas.

Squirrel tree frog, *Hyla squirella*—southeastern Virginia to the Keys and west to Lousiana and southeastern Texas.

CHORUS FROGS
(Family Hylidae)

Boreal chorus frog, *Pseudacris triseriata maculata*—northern Ontario west to Great Bear Lake, south through Utah and Colorado and, intermixed with the Western chorus frog, from northern peninsula of Michigan to Nebraska.

Ornate chorus frog, *Pseudacris ornata*—Coastal Plain from North Carolina to eastern Louisiana and south through most of Florida.

Southern chorus frog, *Pseudacris nigrita nigrita*—eastern North Carolina to northern Florida and southern Mississippi.

Western chorus frog, *Pseudacris triseriata triseriata*—western New York and extreme southern Quebec to Kansas and Oklahoma. There are some isolated colonies in New Mexico and Arizona.

CRICKET FROGS
(Family Hylidae)

Northern cricket frog, *Acris crepitans crepitans*—Long Island south to Louisiana and eastern Texas.

Southern cricket frog, *Acris gryllus gryllus*—southeastern Virginia, south to Gulf Coast and Mississippi River.

SPADEFOOT TOADS
(Family Pelobatidae)

Couch's spadefoot, *Scaphiopus couchi*—central Texas and Oklahoma west to Arizona and south into Mexico.

145

Eastern spadefoot, *Scaphiopus holbrooki*—southern New England to southern Florida and Key West, west to southeastern Missouri, Arkansas and Louisiana. Not found in most upland areas in the South.

Hurter's spadefoot, *Scaphiopus hurteri*—central Arkansas and western Louisiana to central Oklahoma and southern Texas.

Western spadefoot, *Scaphiopus hammondi*—Great Valley and Coastal Range south of San Francisco south to Baja California. East into Colorado, New Mexico and western Oklahoma, south into Mexico.

(Family Leptodactylidae)

Barking frog, *Eleutherodactylus augusti latrans*—central Texas and southeastern New Mexico.

Greenhouse frog, *Eleutherodactylus ricordi planirostris*—introduced into Florida from Cuba and several of the West Indies.

(Family Microhylidae)

Eastern narrow-mouthed toad, *Gastrophryne carolinensis*—southern Maryland to Florida Keys, west to Missouri and eastern Texas. There is an isolated colony in Iowa.

Sheep frog, *Hypopachus cuneus cuneus*—southern Texas to Veracruz.

(Family Ascaphidae)

Tailed frog, *Ascaphus truei*—primarily west of the Cascade Mountains, from southwestern British Columbia to Mendocino County, California. In the Rocky Mountains of Idaho and Montana, and extreme southeastern Washington and northeastern Oregon.

Bibliography

BOOKS

Audubon Nature Encyclopedia, The. Curtis Publishing Company, 1965 and 1966.

Cochran, Doris M. *Living Amphibians of the World,* Doubleday & Company, 1961.

Conant, Roger. *A Field Guide to Reptiles and Amphibians of the United States and Canada East of the 100th Meridian,* Houghton Mifflin Company, 1958.

Cruickshank, Allan D., Kitchen, Herman W., Mohr, Charles E., Platt, Rutherford, Ross, Edward S. *Hunting With the Camera,* Harper & Brothers, 1957.

Dickerson, Mary C. *The Frog Book,* Doubleday, Doran & Company, Inc., 1931.

Kinne, Russ. *The Complete Book of Nature Photography,* A. S. Barnes & Company, Inc., 1962.

Moore, Clifford B. *The Book of Wild Pets,* Charles T. Branford Company, 1954.

Noble, G. Kingsley. *The Biology of the Amphibia,* McGraw-Hill Book Company, 1931.

Oliver, James A. *The Natural History of North American Amphibians and Reptiles,* D. Van Nostrand Company, Inc., 1955.

Stebbins, Robert C. *Amphibians of Western North America,* University of California Press, 1951.

Stebbins, Robert C. *Amphibians and Reptiles of Western North America,* McGraw-Hill Book Company, 1954.

Stebbins, Robert C. *A Field Guide to Western Reptiles and Amphibians,* Houghton Mifflin Company, 1966.

Stone, Witmer. *Plants of Southern New Jersey,* Report of New Jersey State Museum, 1910.

Wright, Albert Hazen, and Wright, Anna Allen. *Handbook of Frogs and Toads of the United States and Canada,* Comstock Publishing Company, Inc., 1949.

ARTICLES

Bentley, P. J. "Adaptations of Amphibia to Arid Environments," *Science,* Vol. 152, April 1966.

Smith, Philip W. "The Amphibians and Reptiles of Illinois," *Illinois Natural History Survey Bulletin,* Vol. 28, Article 1, 1961.

Storm, Robert M. *Endangered Plants and Animals of Oregon, No. 11— Amphibians and Reptiles, Special Report 206,* January 1966, Agricultural Experiment Station, Oregon State University.

RECORDINGS

Allen, Arthur A., and Kellogg, Peter P. *Voices of the Night,* Cornell University Records, a Division of Cornell University Press, Ithaca, N.Y.

Bogert, Charles M. *Sounds of North American Frogs,* Folkway Records & Service Corporation, 117 West 46 Street, New York City, 1958.

Index

149

Index

Index